ELEVEN LOURDES MIRACLES

This book describes the results of an examination of medical documents put forward by the Lourdes Medical Bureau as evidence of the miraculous nature of certain cures. The author, who is Hon. Experimental Research Officer to the Society for Psychical Research, carried out the investigation under a grant from the Parapsychology Foundation of New York.

ELEVEN LOURDES MIRACLES

by

D. J. WEST
M.B., CH.B., D.P.M.

GERALD DUCKWORTH & CO., LTD.
3 Henrietta Street, London, W.C.2.

PRINTED IN GREAT BRITAIN
BY EBENEZER BAYLIS AND SON, LTD., THE
TRINITY PRESS, WORCESTER, AND LONDON

CONTENTS

INTRODUCTION

THE topic of faith-healing has once again come to prominence in public discussions, and once again a Church of England Commission is engaged in examining the evidence concerning it. The subject is of interest to the parapsychologist because the supposedly 'inexplicable' or 'miraculous' element in faith cures might be analogous to the 'psi' effects attributed to mediums and to psychically gifted persons.

Unfortunately the facts are elusive. Although a plethora of accounts of cures appear in popular books and magazines they hardly ever contain sufficiently precise medical details to enable a doctor to form a reasonable judgment. If one tries to follow up such reports with a view to collecting the essential medical facts one soon finds investigation blocked by numerous obstructions. Not least of the difficulties is the extreme reluctance of doctors and hospital authorities to divulge medical information about their patients. The recent investigation by Dr Louis Rose, who tried to follow up many of the spectacular cures attributed to the spirit healer Harry Edwards, illustrates the enormous difficulties that confront the inquirer. Dr Rose had to give a very great amount of time to following up alleged cures for the sake of a very small yield of interesting cases (37).

Such has been my own experience, although on a much smaller scale, when on occasions I have tried to obtain confirmation of remarkable faith cures reported to the Society for Psychical Research. Either the patient does not want the family doctor to know of his connection with the healer, or else the doctor does not care to enter into discussion on the matter. In a recent instance, a faith healer was introduced to me and gave me the names of six persons who, according to her, had all been cured in extraordinary fashion as a result of her ministrations. In only one of these cases was the doctor's evidence obtainable, and according to the doctor in that case nothing remarkable had happened. Such is the common outcome of inquiries of this type. Indeed, scientific evidence on faith healing of any description has always been hard to come by, and such evidence as is available lends but little support to the widespread belief in the existence of a powerful curative factor not yet understood. A recent pamphlet by the British Medical Association on the subject of Divine Healing amply bears this out (7). In spite of affirmation by many doctors of their faith in such powers, and in spite of their obvious desire to support the teachings of the Church, the actual evidence adduced for real cures was admittedly poor indeed. In France, Noël Bayon has compiled an amusing and critical survey of the activities of unorthodox healers without coming across any serious evidence. He even went so far as to set up himself as a healer and collected many testimonials to his (bogus) powers (3).

In spite of disappointing experiences in the past, I welcomed the opportunity afforded by the generosity of the Parapsychology Foundation of New York to survey the evidence for cures at Lourdes because I felt that there the situation is different. This Roman Catholic shrine is uniquely favoured in possessing a Medical Bureau the function of which is to collect and sift the medical facts of any cures reported to have taken place at or in connection with the holy waters of Lourdes. The files at the Lourdes Medical Bureau contain an accumulation of medical data on faith cures that has no parallel elsewhere.

The Lourdes cures receive increasing publicity through the books of Roman Catholic writers and from popular accounts in the press, but scarcely any independent medical comment has appeared in recent years. This silence does not necessarily mean that doctors consider the question unworthy of serious consideration, for as recent letters to the *British Medical Journal* have shown some doctors take the Lourdes cures very seriously. But the emotional aura of religious controversy that surrounds Lourdes tends to detract from the purely medical interest of the alleged events and to obscure the actual facts. Those attracted to Lourdes' cures are usually more interested in confirming their religious or political opinions than in studying the facts for their own sake. Conversely, those interested in medical research do not choose Lourdes as an object of study on account of the emotionalism and controversy. So in the end there is much publicity but very little unbiased study of the raw material. This present contribution aims, if not to fill the gap, at least to put something into it.

The tendency to stray away from the facts is by no means limited to those with a religious faith in the cures. One sceptical medical specialist, to whom I submitted the details of a case for his opinion, produced pages and pages of comment on the role of the Catholic Church in modern politics, and only after much persuasion did he eventually turn his attention to medical business. Two French doctors, Thérèse and Guy Valot, have recently written a quite interesting critical commentary on Lourdes, but not content with discussing such relevant facts about the cures as they have been able to ascertain, they find it necessary to drag into their criticisms of the Lourdes claims such irrelevant matters as the poor quality of the Medical Bureau's library in comparison with their own (p. 33) and the fact that the Pope saw fit to receive Gina Lollobrigida, an actress whom (in their ignorance) they criticize as having sex appeal without talent (p. 121) (44).

In contrast, as many as sixty years ago, the Society for Psychical Research published a critical study of Lourdes cures, at once balanced and factual, carried out by F. W. H. Myers and Dr A. T. Myers (33). These investigators were sceptical of the worth of the evidence then available, but today, with objective medical tests so much more developed and more frequently applied, one would expect the position to be radically changed.

The present study is concerned solely with the evidence relating to remarkable or unexplained cures, the aim being to keep as far as possible to factual matters and to limit discussion to a consideration of the plausibility or otherwise of various natural interpretations. The fact that these particular cures are believed to have religious significance is irrelevant to the purpose of the study. A critical survey of the factual evidence would be equally valid whether the cures were brought about by a new drug or by the intervention of the Virgin Mary. Nevertheless, in order to appreciate fully the nature of the medical documents that form the material of this study, I give in Chapter I a brief outline of the circumstances that brought them into existence. I wish to extend my sincere thanks to the following persons who have helped me in various ways in the preparation of this report. None of them are responsible for any of the views expressed.

Group-Captain L. Cheshire, V.C.	Mrs Dorothee Koestler
Dr M. Conran	Dr Stephanie Leece
Dr I. Fletcher	Dr Eunice Lockey
Dr R. S. Francis	Dr D. O. O'Connell
Dr D. Garrow	Dr C. M. H. Pedler
Colonel C. H. Green	Dr Una Pedler
Miss Joan Harris	Dr Paul Vasse
Dr S. Kalinsky	Dr I. G. Wickes
Dr J. Kappers	

I wish also to place on record my considerable indebtedness to Dr H. Grenet, President of the Lourdes International Medical Committee, and to the Lourdes Medical Bureau, for placing at my unrestricted disposal the medical dossiers of the recent miracle cures.

The extracts from the documents which are reproduced in this book were translated by the author with the kind assistance of Mrs Dorothee Koestler.

Finally, I have especially to thank Mrs. Eileen J. Garrett without whose interest and generous help no investigation would have been contemplated.

I

THE BACKGROUND

IN February, 1858 a local peasant girl, Bernadette Soubirous, gathering wood near the River Gave, at the foot of a cliff known as Massabieille, had a vision of the Virgin Mary standing in an opening in the rock. This opening has become the famous healing grotto, and sick persons desiring to solicit the Virgin for a miraculous cure come in their thousands to bathe in the waters at the foot of the Massabieille. Cures were said to commence only a few weeks after the first apparition of the Virgin, and they have been continuing ever since.

In 1858 a neighbouring healing shrine of the Virgin was already functioning at Bétharram, and there was another well-known one at La Salette, near Grenoble, but in the course of time Lourdes has outstripped all other centres of pilgrimage (25). Today, an impressive basilica surmounts the Massabieille, and special buildings have been constructed to house the baths, to accommodate the sick, and to provide a Medical Bureau. Dr Leuret, the late President of the Medical Bureau, reports that 2,200,000 pilgrims and 15,800 sick visited Lourdes in 1948, and 3,000,000 pilgrims and over 20,000 sick in 1949. The numbers are increasing every year, and Lourdes has become a considerable centre of tourist and souvenir industries. Dr Thérèse Valot suggests that even these enormous numbers under-estimate the truth, since many visitors to Lourdes are not registered at the hotels and many sick persons come on their own initiative apart from the organized pilgrimage trains (44).

As far back as 1885 Dr SaintMaclou instituted a rudimentary medical office at Lourdes for inquiring into the cures. He was succeeded in this work by Drs Boissarie, Le Bec, Marchand, Vallet and Leuret, all of whom have published books on the

1

cures (6, 19, 22, 28, 29, 39–43). The most recent period is the most relevant to the present study. In 1947, the new Bishop of Lourdes, Monseigneur Théas, brought about a reorganization of the Medical Bureau. Dr Fr. Leuret became the new President, and in addition, a National Medical Commission (since become an International Commission) was formed to act as a sort of second tribunal.

The International Medical Commission is a committee of doctors that sits in Paris and has the last word in deciding whether a cure is inexplicable from the medical standpoint. After being passed by this Commission the case still has to be considered by the ecclesiastical authorities before being officially pronounced 'miraculous'.

With the reorganization of the Medical Bureau came a definite attempt to examine cases before as well as after their cure. Sick pilgrims visit the medical office and in cases in which the certificates they bring from their own doctors are insufficient to make the diagnosis clear they can be examined by the doctors at Lourdes. There are now facilities at the Lourdes Bureau for taking X-rays and electrocardiographs, as well as for performing all kinds of clinical examinations.

Dr Leuret records that over a period of three years the Lourdes office received and recorded medical observations on more than 3,000 patients. 'And this effort is not wasted for, in 1949, we had the good fortune to register the cure (which will not, however, be official until after the second examination in 1950) of a little girl of three suffering from cerebral diplegia since birth, whom we had actually examined three days before her cure.' Apparently the cure was not confirmed, because no account of it has been published, and Dr Grenet, President of the International Commission, told me he did not know of the case. I have been able to discover no other instance in which a cured patient has been examined by the Lourdes Bureau both before and after the event.

According to Dr Leuret's own description, the Lourdes dossiers are compiled in the following way. As soon as a recovery is reported, the patient is seen and examined at the Medical Bureau. On this occasion, the medical certificates which the patient has brought with him on the pilgrimage are studied, the patient's story and the testimony of witnesses to his cure are recorded, and as far as possible his present condition and his condition before the cure are assessed. A case reporter is appointed from among the available doctors, who presents the case before a full meeting of the Medical Bureau, at which visiting doctors are allowed to be present and take part in the discussion.

If the case appears to the doctors to be sufficiently striking, a doctor from the region where the patient lives is entrusted with the task of following up the case and collecting further testimony. The patient is recalled for a second examination a year later. The doctors come to an opinion whether, in the light of all the evidence, the case still seems inexplicable. Their opinion is recorded on the dossier and they sign their names to it. If the case is passed, the dossier is then forwarded to the International Medical Commission at Paris, who appoint a reporter to study the case and to present the pros and cons of the evidence for their consideration. The International Commission considers the case from the technical point of view and decides whether, in their opinion, the cure seems completely inexplicable, in which event they submit the whole dossier to the Archbishop to whose diocese the healed person belongs. He appoints a Canonical Commission, which is an ecclesiastical body, to make fresh inquiry into all the circumstances of the case. They take depositions from the witnesses, and come to an opinion whether or not the case meets the Church's own criteria for a miracle. Only if the Canonical Commission comes to a favourable conclusion does the Archbishop, after due consideration, pronounce that the cure was due to the miraculous intervention of the Virgin Mary.

Dr Leuret states that the numbers of cases that passed an initial examination and the numbers of them that were finally accepted by the Lourdes Bureau and passed on to the Medical Commission were, in the years 1946, 1947 and 1948, respectively 36 and 4; 75 and 6; 83 and 9.

Thus a potential cure risks rejection at any of three stages. First, the Lourdes Medical Bureau itself, when the case is

reviewed on the patient's return a year after the first report of
the apparent cure, may decide that it is not worth while to bring
the matter to the attention of higher authority. Second, the
Medical Commission in Paris may reject a case passed by the
Lourdes Bureau. Third and last, an Ecclesiastical Commission
may reject the case in spite of the doctors' views.

The following figures are given by Leuret and Bon (22) and
Boissarie de l'Epine (6). In the year 1946, of 36 cases that had
been retained for further consideration, the Lourdes Bureau
rejected 32 and passed on 4 for consideration by the Medical
Commission. In 1947 they rejected 69 out of 75 cases recon-
sidered and recommended six to the Medical Commission. Of
these six the Medical Commission accepted only one (Mlle
Malgogne). In 1948 the Lourdes Bureau passed 9 out of 83
potential cases. In 1949 the Medical Commission accepted
3 cases (Gérard Baillie, Thérèse Canin and Rose Martin) and
rejected 3. In 1950 they accepted 2 (Mme Gibault and Jeanne
Fretel) and rejected 9. Of the six cases named above as having
passed the higher medical authority only three have been
pronounced miraculous by Ecclesiastical Authority.

Since 1946, when the procedure of Canonical Commissions
was resumed after a break of thirty-three years, and up to the
time of writing this report in 1956, only eleven cases have passed
all three tribunals and been pronounced miraculous.

Each Lourdes dossier includes several forms. The first page
contains the details of age, occupation, address, diagnosis and
dates of visits to the Lourdes Bureau. A second form records
the results of the first examination, the patient's history and
the testimony relating to the cure. There is a separate form
for recording the results of the second examination a year later
and for the report from the doctor entrusted with the investigation of the case. Finally, above the signatures of the doctors
present at the meeting which decides whether the case should
be passed, a form containing the following five questions has
to be filled in:

1. Is it certain that the illness described in the certificates
was present at the time of the pilgrimage to Lourdes?

2. Was the course of the illness suddenly changed at a time when there was no tendency towards improvement?
3. Has there been a cure? Did the cure take place without the use of medicaments?
4. Is there any reason for postponing a final opinion?
5. Is this cure susceptible to a medical explanation? Is it outside natural laws?

Signatures:

Date:

This questionnaire is designed to meet the requirements of Canonical Commissions, who decide whether a cure is miraculous according to the criteria laid down by Pope Benedict XIV in his treatise on Beatification and Canonization. He enumerates seven conditions all of which should be fulfilled:

1. That the illness should be serious, and impossible, or at least very difficult, to cure.
2. That the illness should not be on the decline or of such a nature that it might in any case improve.
3. That no medication should have been given, or if it has been given, that its inefficacy should be clearly established.
4. That the cure should be sudden, instantaneous.
5. That the cure should be complete.
6. That the cure should not correspond to a crisis in the illness brought about by natural causes.
7. That after the cure there should be no recurrence of the illness in question.

Dr Leuret was not altogether happy at the exclusion from the possibility of being authenticated of miraculous cures in which traces of the original complaint remained. One remarkable case which particularly interested him, and which he published in his book, that of the boy Gérard Baillie, was rejected by a Canonical Commission on the grounds that sight was not perfectly restored. On the other hand, the case of the boy Francis Pascal was pronounced miraculous in spite of the fact that his visual acuity remained considerably subnormal, and the cure of the arthritic Mlle Clauzel was also pronounced miraculous in spite of persistence of the signs of arthritis in her X-rays. The Canonical Commissions must allow a certain latitude in the interpretation of the criteria for a miraculous cure, but the existence of these formal rules explains the rather specialized orientation of much of the discussion on the cures. While the outsider is primarily concerned about whether a natural explanation of the cure could be discovered, the Lourdes doctors and the Canonical Commissions are deeply concerned with certain formal criteria which have no direct relevance to the scientific evaluation of the cure.

In theory the procedure for verifying the cures is very rigorous. A minimum of a year is required for following up the case and collecting the evidence. Three independent tribunals weigh the pros and cons and consider the evidence. The final ecclesiastical tribunal contains non-medical men who can consider the evidence from the logical as well as the technical standpoint. All this sounds excellent. How it works in practice will be seen later when actual cases are discussed. The system certainly sounds impressive, and is frequently cited by apologists of the miraculous as almost proof in itself of the authenticity of the cures. Thus Marcel Ligny writes: 'One scarcely sees how, under these conditions, errors or deceptions could creep in, despite the efforts (and they are numerous and resourceful) of the enemies of Lourdes to bring them about for the purposes of exploitation.' (24)

The present study was scheduled to begin in July, 1954. I met Dr Leuret in April, 1954, at the Parapsychology Foundation Conference on unorthodox healing held at St Paul de Vence, and with great enthusiasm he promised to furnish me with enough material for several books. His sudden and tragic death a few days later disorganized the arrangements at the Lourdes Bureau and delayed the investigation considerably.

I wrote to the Lourdes Bureau first in July, 1954, but it was not until November that I received in answer to my request photostat copies of the first four dossiers. I at once requested more dossiers, and asked if I could visit the Lourdes Bureau in person to study the original files. It was explained to me that unfortunately the Bureau was only open during the summer months, the season of the pilgrimages. Happily, Mlle Leuret, daughter of the late President, and former secretary of the Bureau, consented to meet me in Paris in January, 1955, and supplied me with more dossiers. At the same time I was able to meet Dr Grenet, President of the International Medical Commission, and also Dr Poumailloux, a member of the Commission. They received me most courteously, but were unable to give me any additional information about the cures, since all the documents were at Lourdes. However, through a member of the Commission residing in London, the radiologist Dr O'Connell, they kindly gave me access to the duplicated summaries of the three cases under consideration by the Commission in 1955. In June, 1955, I was able to visit Lourdes and make a study of the original dossiers. I asked Dr Grenet if he could help me to find out some further medical details relating to certain miracle cases, in particular that of Jeanne Fretel. He promised to try, but nothing came of it. Dr Poumailloux explained to me that the Lourdes authorities were at the mercy of doctors who might withhold information through lack of interest or positive antagonism. Frenchmen as a whole are very reluctant to enter into correspondence, and I have been unable to obtain, save in one or two exceptional cases, any more information than is contained in the dossiers themselves. But this limitation has not affected the primary task, which was to study the evidence already available.

The most interesting assessment of Lourdes cases prior to the period of Dr Leuret's presidency was carried out by a group of French Catholic specialists whose reports were published in 1947 by the Cahiers Laennec in Paris. The work has been translated by Dom Peter Flood and published in Eire (4). The work was carried out under the auspices of the Catholic Medical Society of St Luke, and although the doctors in question all accept the miracles in principle, they make a number of revealing comments.

They drew their information mainly from published accounts of cures. At the time of their investigation 'there were no archives, no documents and no case histories at Lourdes. It was only by means of oral traditions, most of which were supplied by Canon Courtin and Canon René Gael, that the workers were able to get on the tracks of the cases' (p. 175).

They were forced to reject the majority of cases as lacking in information necessary to form a conclusion. Dr Merlin, an ophthalmologist, who dealt with cures of affections of the eyes, complained that the case histories were generally incomplete and insufficiently precise, and they were all old cases—pre-1914 (p. 177). Dr Laffitte (18) mentioned the effect of exaggerated enthusiasm taking away the scientific value of testimony. For instance, in the famous case of de Rudder's fractured leg, Dr van Hoestenberghe's certificate states that by taking hold of the heel it was possible to turn the limb more than once round its axis, and Dr Laffitte comments: 'This is a medical impossibility which is enough to rob a medical observation of all scientific value . . .' Dr Jullien, who dealt with cases of pulmonary tuberculosis (which form a high proportion of Lourdes cures) explains that before about 1925 X-rays and bacteriological tests were not in general use except by specialists, and so the diagnosis was often open to doubt. He describes in detail the case of the Abbé D., one of his own patients, who improved after a visit to Lourdes, but he criticizes strongly the comments of the doctors who examined the man at Lourdes. Their findings were incorrect and incompetent, and their interpretations exaggerated (16). In his summing up, Dr Béhague pleads for proper records to be kept at Lourdes, and for a secretary at Lourdes to direct cured persons to visit the appropriate specialist who alone is competent to interpret all the findings and to give a valid judgment (p. 246).

My object in abstracting these criticisms is to show that up to 1946 Catholic doctors themselves admit many serious shortcomings in the collection of evidence on Lourdes cures. Although it is not worth reporting in detail, I have in fact studied much of the published work concerning earlier years at Lourdes and I heartily endorse the critical comments made by these Catholic specialists. In fact I would go much further and say that it would be a waste of time to rake up a lot of old cases and argue about them now. One need only compare the descriptions of the same alleged events and the same cases in the books of Catholic and anti-Catholic writers to realize that the true facts are irretrievably distorted and overlaid by passionate argument.

One short example must suffice to illustrate this point—the famous case of Pierre de Rudder, a Belgian workman, who is said to have been instantaneously healed of a chronically suppurating fracture of the left leg on the occasion of a visit to the Catholic shrine at Oostacker in 1875. Dr Laffitte, in his report to the Medical Society of St Luke (18), which has already been mentioned, shows himself completely convinced by this miracle. Although he regrets the misplaced enthusiasm of Rudder's medical practitioner, Dr Hoestenberghe, whose observations were exaggerated and inaccurate, Dr Laffitte thinks the facts speak for themselves and show that healing work which would normally require weeks or months took place instantaneously, and therefore miraculously, in Rudder's case. In contrast, the critic Joseph McCabe asserts that the evidence is quite insufficient (25). He rightly draws attention to the fact that the inquiry into the cure and the chief medical certificates were made seventeen years after the event. The alleged persistence of the fracture unhealed up to just before the cure rests on the memory of two or three peasants. Only years after the cure does Dr Hoestenberghe assign a date to his last examination of Rudder, and then he puts it at 'two or three months' before the visit to Oostacker. Dr Roger, who includes a study of the case in a book published in 1934 (36), points out that it was Rudder's left leg that was broken, whereas Dr Hoestenberghe describes the right leg as completely cured after the miracle, with the inner surface of the tibia bone smooth and without fault. Postmortem examination showed that this was not true of the left leg, for the fragments of bone at the site of the old fracture are angulated and displaced and united by a visible lump of callus. Dr Roger also points out that Rudder could walk, although only with the aid of crutches, even before the miracle. Moreover he had been in receipt of a pension for his injury which had stopped with the death of his patron the Vicomte du Bus, so there was a possible motive for his miraculous recovery.

No good purpose would be served and nothing would be likely to be settled by re-opening old controversies of this sort. For this reason I have found it more profitable to concentrate attention on cases in which the evidence has been collected and appraised after 1946 when, as already described, the procedure for official verification was put on a more systematic basis.

II

THE ASSESSMENT OF FAITH CURES

IN studying these cures I had in mind one primary question: does the evidence suggest that at Lourdes recoveries take place of a remarkable kind, such as are not ordinarily encountered in medical experience? I did not expect to reach a final and scientifically conclusive verdict, but simply to arrive at a common-sense judgment based on clinical considerations and on estimation of the reliability of the medical testimony proffered by the Lourdes authorities. An affirmative answer would demonstrate the need for further inquiry on more rigorously scientific lines.

The Roman Catholic authorities are not so much concerned with demonstrating a positive and hitherto unexplained effect as in asserting that the cures are miraculous, that is to say outside the ordinary laws of nature. Consequently they are always searching for cures of the apparently incurable and for miraculously rapid changes in physical state. But from the medical standpoint one need not set the target so high, for even if it is not actually 'miraculous', faith healing might still contain a positive element deserving of scientific study.

Ideally, one would like to be able to compare groups of Lourdes pilgrims with matching groups of patients of similar age and with similar conditions who elected to stay at home. This cannot be done, for unfortunately we have no information at all about the general run of sick who visit Lourdes. We do not know if their recovery rate differs significantly from that of comparable groups of patients elsewhere. We have information solely on that very tiny minority of pilgrims who report dramatic recoveries. Consequently, we have to form a judgment on the basis of a few highly selected cases, and this limitation constitutes a considerable handicap.

11

In the first place, a single cure picked out from thousands of sick has to be very unusual indeed before one feels that it was not just a case of spontaneous recovery happening by chance to coincide with the Lourdes visit. Even very malignant cancers, which are generally regarded as invariably fatal, do in fact (although very rarely) sometimes recover spontaneously. If such sufferers continue to visit Lourdes in sufficient numbers, by sheer chance one would expect sooner or later that a 'miraculous' cancer recovery will be reported. The same consideration applies even more forcibly to cures of conditions like pulmonary tuberculosis, in which spontaneous recoveries are not particularly rare.

In evaluating a cure one can only be guided by what is generally accepted as the usual outcome of such an illness. But the criteria of prognosis in medicine are far from infallible. Because spontaneous and unexplained recoveries from malignant disease are not usually reported in medical journals—either because they are automatically attributed to faulty diagnosis or because they are regarded as curiosities without particular scientific interest—the impression can be built up that recoveries are rarer than is in fact the case. An example of this is the condition, myasthenia gravis, so named because it was once thought to be almost always fatal. Today it is recognized that there are many mild and spontaneously remitting cases, so that the condition does not always merit its gloomy name. All experienced clinicians know that illnesses in real life tend to be more complicated and variable than textbook cases.

On the matter of spontaneous cures the British Medical Association recently published some comments in a pamphlet prepared by their Committee on Divine Healing. The Medical Association's advice had been sought on this and other points by the Archbishop's Commission on Divine Healing. In order to investigate the matter the Association sent a questionary to all its members asking, among other things, if they had had experience of illness in which there had been recovery from apparently incurable disorder. The replies were inconclusive. Some doctors quoted cases of spontaneous cure of what was considered malignant disease, but these were unsubstantiated by microscopical evidence. But the Committee's attention was drawn to the existence of a type of skin tumour clinically and microscopically indistinguishable from the malignant cancerous growth known as primary squamous carcinoma, which nevertheless can be seen to heal spontaneously. They draw the obvious conclusion that 'in other organs of the body also (e.g. stomach, lung, breast) there may be varieties which heal spontaneously and cannot be observed' (48).

At Lourdes, at least in modern times, the 'miracles' reported are not of a type that an outside would consider self-evidently miraculous. There are no cases of lost eyes or amputated legs sprouting anew. In the nature of things it is the chronic sick who make pilgrimages, persons in whom a protracted struggle has already been waged between the powers of resistance and the forces of disease. The cures claimed mostly consist in a sudden tipping of the balance in favour of the patient, whose recuperative powers seemed suddenly to reassert themselves. There are very few cases of recovery from essentially incurable disease, and very many cases of dramatically swift recovery from serious but potentially curable conditions like tuberculosis. (An analysis of the diagnoses in recent published cases is given later in this report.)

Speed of recovery has been put forward many times as the essential and 'miraculous' element in Lourdes cures. The recuperative process is normal, healing occurs in natural fashion, wounds do not just disappear, they are replaced by scars, but the whole chain of events is either instantaneous or unnaturally rapid (12, 13, 18, 22).

In the case of a visible wound, competent witnesses can supply the testimony necessary to establish the duration of the healing process. In the case of internal organic conditions (such as tuberculosis) it takes either X-rays or very skilled medical examination to detect the healing changes. In most cases no claims can fairly be made about the speed of the cure unless the patient is subjected to rigorous comparative examination immediately before and immediately after the alleged cure. Unfortunately this never happens. Instead, the patient gets up and walks, or gives some other indication of feeling better, and then, some time later, he is examined and found to be improved. The whole improvement is then attributed to the few moments at Lourdes when the patient 'felt better'. In reality the improvement could have taken place at a steady rate over the whole period since the patient was last examined (which is often a long time prior to the cure). As everyone knows, the subjective sensation of 'feeling better' is no sure index of the real state of affairs. At the end of a long illness subjective symptoms often drag on long after the cause has been remedied. 'Feeling better' at Lourdes might mean no more than that the powerful suggestive influence of the shrine, the ritual processions and the expectant atmosphere served to remove an overlay of psychological symptoms that had hitherto masked a real organic improvement. On this matter of speed of recovery many claims are made but few are substantiated.

Since the cures reported are selected from a large and mixed population of chronic sick, one cannot expect the patients to have been medically investigated with the same thoroughness and precision as would be the case if they formed material for research project in a modern hospital. Some doctors whom I have asked to consider reports from Lourdes have replied that in the absence of hospital tests and investigations the exact nature of the illnesses are uncertain and therefore no scientific opinion can be given. I feel that in one sense their attitude is correct, in another it is mistaken. They are certainly correct in maintaining that no final scientific conclusion can be reached on this basis, but at least some preliminary impression can be gained from case reports—provided, of course, they are detailed, competent and unbiased.

The question becomes even more difficult if one tries to take into account the highly emotive quality of the testimony in the Lourdes cases. To the people who supply the evidence, both the lay witnesses and the doctors, it is not just a medical matter, whether one form of treatment is superior to another, it is a question whether they have been privileged to see the Hand of God at work producing a divine miracle. For them the decision is a deeply personal one involving their religious faith, their moral outlook, their Church's ordinances and in some cases their political affiliations. To expect witnesses under such pressure to give straightforward, unbiased accounts would be absurd. In investigating other types of alleged spontaneous psychic experience parapsychologists have learned the necessity for preserving rigorous canons of objective corroboration. When a supposedly supernormal element is in question, the evidence has to be sifted and the testimony checked and counter-checked to an extent that would be superfluous in the consideration of some simple, non-emotive question.

Strictly speaking, the sympathetic but severely analytical approach to testimony exemplified in some of the publications of the Society for Psychical Research (9, 47) should be applied to the Lourdes evidence. Since that ideal is clearly unattainable, I have given up all attempts to apply such criteria to the Lourdes evidence. Instead, I have accepted largely at its face value the documentary evidence offered by the Lourdes Bureau, and have gone on to consider what these documents suggest assuming that they are accurate. Except in clear cases of inconsistency and contradiction, I have not sought to challenge the facts as stated. If, for example, it is said that a fever subsided on such and such a day, I accept the statement and do not inquire into the time the note was made, the reliability of the person who used the thermometer, the possibility of malingering by the patient, or the possibility of lying by the witness. While no miracle case could be proved to the satisfaction of psychical investigators without inquiries of this kind, I have thought it wiser in the first instance simply to consider the evidence on the lines that a doctor might consider the history given him by a patient in the course of a consultation. The doctor is not so much concerned with scientific proof as he is desirous of arriving at a clinical impression as to the most likely interpretation of the patient's story. It is only if the Lourdes stories really do suggest something odd and anomalous, or some as yet un-recognized principle, that one need go on to demand further cases in which there is continuous hospital investigation and closer scrutiny of witnesses' testimony.

III

THE PSYCHOLOGICAL FACTOR

WAS there a real physical change or was it all psychological? This question, the first that springs to everyone's mind at the mention of faith cure, becomes more and more difficult to answer the more one learns about the connections between mental attitudes and disease processes.

In raising this question most people have in mind those relatively straightforward cases of hysteria in which the patient, without fully realizing what he is doing, imitates the symptoms of physical disease. The hysteric with a pseudo-paralysed arm, for instance, will hold his muscles stiff and rigid and assert with complete conviction that he cannot move the limb. As is now well known, this sort of trouble often yields instantly to impressive treatments that capture the patient's imagination. Cases of hysteria provide ready subjects for unorthodox manipulations, hypnosis, and faith-healing, for all of these techniques use suggestion to great effect. But since recoveries of this kind imply no more than a change in the patient's attitude of mind— and sometimes a very superficial change at that—they are not considered remarkable or indicative of any unexplained process, and the Lourdes Medical Bureau officially refuses to consider cases in which an hysterical element features prominently. As will be seen when the actual cases are discussed, it is a matter of opinion whether the Bureau succeeds in excluding all hysterical cases, but that they should be eliminated everyone seems to be agreed.

The question of the elimination of hysterical cases still tends to dominate the arguments of both the antagonists and the protagonists of Lourdes cures. In reality this task represents no more than the first and easiest step in the process of disentangling what can be explained on present-day psychological principles.

16

As a result of the rapid development of the speciality called psycho-somatic medicine, which is the study of the influence of thought processes on the development and course of physical disorders, doctors have come to recognize that human ailments simply will not conform to our neat concepts of mental illness on the one hand and physical illness on the other. Psychological factors may aggravate or precipitate real and severe physical disorders, and, in the opposite direction, organic conditions at one time believed immune from psychological influences do sometimes improve as a result of the patient's changed mental outlook. Of course there are limits to psycho-somatic influences, and doctors are still hotly debating where to put them, but the fact remains that the range of possible psychological effects far exceeds what was at one time thought possible.

In some cases the influence of mental attitude is minimal. In a cholera epidemic, for instance, in which the majority who are exposed to the infection succumb, the individual's previous mental history and present state of mind seem unimportant. In contrast, in circumstances in which the individual's personal resistance to the disease plays an important part, as it does in pulmonary tuberculosis, state of mind may be very relevant.

Much has been learned in recent years about the deleterious bodily effects of certain emotional states. One can easily see how a chronic state of depression, which takes away the appetite and leads to loss of weight, will weaken stamina and lower resistance to infection, but emotional disturbance produces many more subtle effects. Many bodily processes—respiration, blood circulation, growth, digestion—go their own way regardless of our wishes. They are regulated by the autonomic part of the nervous system and by the secretions of the endocrine glands. Neither of these systems comes ordinarily under voluntary control, but both respond sensitively to emotion, and so provide close links between mental and bodily functions.

A familiar example of this link in practice is an individual in a state of alarm. His heart beats faster, his blood pressure rises, blood is diverted from the gut to the head and limbs, muscles stiffen in preparation for action, respiration quickens, intestinal movements decrease, etc., etc. In fact sudden alarm produces profound effects over the whole body. Sometimes in the case of an individual with a weak heart, and in very rare instances in healthy persons, death from cardiac failure may result from a sudden alarm (10, p. 340).

A long-term effect, more relevant to the causation of disease (and one capable of demonstration by direct observation) is the influence of anxiety on the movement and secretions of the stomach which, if long continued, produces a state of affairs favourable to the development of peptic ulcers. Certain diseases, such as asthma, migraine and many non-infectious rashes are now recognized as being in many cases physiological responses to disturbed emotions. Although, unlike hysterical symptoms, these are genuine physical disorders, they sometimes subside like magic when the patient improves his state of mind through psycho-therapy. Even in severe organic disease—cancer, diabetes, cerebral haemorrhage—which seem far removed from psychology, and in which destructive processes have gone too far for normal function ever to resume, psychological factors may have played a part in the causation of the condition, and psychological factors may sometimes help to arrest the progress of the disease and save the patient's life.

To give a concrete example, emotional tension accompanied by spasm of blood vessels leads to chronically raised blood pressure. This strains the heart and damages the kidneys. Damaged kidneys release toxic substances which further raise blood pressure, causing further strain on the heart and perhaps damage to blood vessels. A vicious circle sets in until eventually heart, blood vessel or kidney breaks down completely and the patient dies. A release of emotional tension will sometimes effect a break in this vicious circle (34). Flanders Dunbar, in her monumental survey of the literature of psycho-somatic medicine (10) quotes one case (p. 355) of a woman of 61 who had had treatment for severe angina pectoris and was not expected to live. Her blood pressure was very high, and after walking only a few steps she would complain of 'pressure on the heart', etc. One day her husband shot himself while she was in the next room. Both doctor and relatives expected the shock to kill her. In reality, the patient had long suffered from her unhappy marriage, although she had not been able to talk about it, and the day after her husband's death she 'joyfully' did a big laundry all on her own in order to distract herself! Instead of collapsing, her blood pressure subsided, her anginal attacks ceased, and she 'remained much better ever since'. The unexpected release of her pent-up emotions probably saved her life.

The study of skin conditions is particularly fruitful in this connection, for skin is both responsive to emotion and easy to watch. Moreover, as the British Medical Association Committee had occasion to observe in connection with skin cancers that recover, what happens on the surface may also happen underneath without our knowing.

Under hypnosis, and given appropriate suggestions, subjects have been known to produce blisters corresponding to imaginary burns and even to develop bruising and oozing of blood from the skin. Some of these experiments have been most carefully conducted. In an important monograph on spontaneous bleeding (38), Dr R. Schindler describes in detail three cases of spontaneous skin haemorrhages of unknown origin in which he succeeded in demonstrating a psychological basis. In all three cases the most careful medical investigations failed to reveal any abnormality in the blood or blood vessels to account for the bleedings, and in each case Dr Schindler found that by means of hypnotic suggestion he could produce bleeding at chosen times and designated spots on parts covered with a plaster cast to prevent cheating. All three of Dr Schindler's patients responded to the psychological approach and were cured. One woman had been bedridden for nearly five years on account of this trouble. A severe fever always accompanied the appearance of her skin lesions, but both disturbances subsided simultaneously as a result of psychological treatment. In comparison with these cases, the cure of intractable nose bleeding, which took place at Lourdes, and is described at length in a paper by Dr Barjon, pales into insignificance (2).

Psychogenic skin conditions, besides providing visible confirmation of bodily responses to emotion, sometimes demonstrate in graphic form how a disorder of function precipitated by emotion (consisting at first perhaps of blood vessel spasm) can in time result in destruction of tissue with ulceration and even gangrene. Ida Macalpine and J. Paterson Ross have recently reported a case (26) of a young woman with long-standing swelling and ulceration of her forearm, so bad indeed that she was sent to the surgeon for amputation. She herself clamoured for the operation. Fortunately the doctors investigated her case with great thoroughness and concluded that no abnormality of the arteries, veins or lymph channels was present which would account for her condition. She was given psychological treatment, and as a result of the insight she gained into her self-destructive feelings her arm cleared up in the magically swift manner so characteristic of psychogenic conditions.

Skin conditions also serve to show how disturbances generally regarded as organic will sometimes respond to psychological influences. A now famous example is Dr A. A. Mason's case of congenital ichthyosis (crocodile skin). A youth who had always suffered from this trouble, which spread all over his body and resisted every form of treatment including skin grafting, came to Dr Mason for hypnotic treatment. As a result of the doctor's suggestions, an immediate and remarkable improvement took place, and Dr Mason later demonstrated the case at the Royal Society of Medicine as an instance of unexpected alleviation. One particularly interesting feature was that Dr Mason's suggestions took the line that first one part would clear, then another, and in fact the skin did clear in stages, area by area, in accord with the suggestions (30).

To sum up, doctors are now prepared to believe that psychological influence plays some part in almost all illnesses and a large part in many. Correlations have been worked out between the incidence of various types of organic disease—fracture, cancer, tuberculosis, coronary thrombosis, etc.—and the personality traits of sick people, with the discovery that certain temperaments have been found to be prone to particular diseases. Then again, having contracted some disease, mental attitude may have an important bearing on the ability to combat the illness and the prospects of recovery. Wittkower has explored this question in detail with regard to tuberculosis (49). Chronically worrying and despondent types do badly, possibly because of the effect on their hormone secretion from the adrenal cortex, which is known to have a relation to the resistance to infection. In rehabilitation from injuries temperament is equally important. A happy, confident man will get back to normal much swifter than a miserable discontent who always keeps half an eye on the compensation figures.

All this may seem a far cry from Lourdes, but one must take into account such facts in order to judge whether recoveries at Lourdes differ in kind from unusual recoveries observed in ordinary medical practice. In the absence of comprehensive statistics as to the frequency of cures among complete groups of pilgrims, one can only arrive at an opinion about a rare cure at Lourdes by considering whether substantially similar cures take place elsewhere as a result of understandable psychological influences. The main lesson which psycho-somatic medicine teaches in this connection is that the power of suggestion is not limited to the removal of the hysteric's imagined physical disabilities; it may also help restore disordered bodily function when this is being caused or aggravated by emotion, and it may also in some cases lead to a palpable amelioration of organic conditions.

The only way to sort out what would be unlikely or impossible for psychological influences to produce is to concentrate on looking for evidence of sudden restoration of structural faults. Almost any cure which involves merely a restoration of function, however striking the physiological change, could in theory be psychogenic. A sudden cure of thyrotoxicosis or even diabetes, which are disorders of endocrine *function*, would no longer seem miraculous. Flanders Dunbar (p. 100) quotes an amusing case of a young woman with thyrotoxicosis (swollen, over-active thyroid, bulging eyes, disordered heart action) who was sent by the surgeon for psychotherapy so that her fears might be calmed in order for her to undergo the necessary operation. After three months' analysis she returned to the surgeon minus her fears and minus the disease.

In view of all these considerations, the necessity for objective evidence of structural changes cannot be over-emphasized. X-rays, measurements and laboratory tests, carried out just before and just after the supposed miraculous change, are essential if some new principle or factor is to be established. Clinical impressions by skilled specialists can go a long way, but for this purpose can never be conclusive. Unless the change shows on the visible surface of the body, scientific tests are essential. The change must be shown to be objective. Changes in symptoms can be most misleading. A dying man can convince himself he is better, a healthy man can think he is dying. Pathology and symptoms do not always go hand in hand. Of two persons with the same amount of destruction of tissue, one may carry on much as usual while the other lapses into hopeless invalidism. The Lourdes Medical Bureau shows no hesitation in claiming miraculous and instantaneous restitution of normality in cases of organic disease involving serious destruction of tissue. If true these large claims should be susceptible to easy verification by objective examinations before and after the cure. How far the Lourdes evidence falls short of these expectations will become apparent in the next section.

IV

THE RECENT MIRACLE CASES

THE Lourdes files contain too many cases for every one to be considered in detail, but fortunately we have a ready-made selection, of what are presumably the most impressive cures, in the eleven modern cases that have passed all three tribunals and been pronounced miraculous. The Canonical Commissions do take into account other factors than purely medical considerations—an increase in religious faith as a result of the cure would be a point in favour of a miracle—but on the whole these eleven cases would appear to provide a fair selection of the most interesting of the modern cures. Accordingly each one is considered in turn.

1. MLLE GABRIELLE CLAUZEL

Most of the dossier on this cure has been published by Drs Leuret and Bon in their book, *Les Guérisons Miraculeuses Modernes* (22). They call the illness 'rheumatic spondylitis with compression of the nerve roots'. The cure was said to have taken place suddenly during Mass on August 15th, 1943. The chief medical document, dated May 21st, 1944, is a report from Dr Maurin, Honorary Surgeon to the Civil Hospital at Oran, who was the patient's own doctor. He writes as follows:

Dr Maurin's Report

Mlle Clauzel, of rue d'Alsace Lorraine, Oran, entered hospital in 1937 for treatment of a recto-vaginal fistula caused by an abscess of haemorrhoidal origin. Recurrence and repeat operation.

During her stay in hospital she had a frank attack of rheumatoid arthritis, especially marked in the region of the left wrist, which was the site of considerable and painful swelling. Other joints also were affected, in particular the articulations of the cervical spine.

(The inflammatory attack subsided after some time and the condition improved further as a result of a stay at Aix-les-Bains. This improved state of affairs lasted for nearly a year after which the patient, who still carried herself stooped, was obliged to take to bed once more. There was no inflammatory attack, as on the first occasion, but she had cervical and lumbar pains.)[1]

An X-ray taken at this time showed osteophytic proliferations (vertebral lippings) and the classic deformation of the vertebral bodies of rheumatic spondylitis.

At this period attacks began to occur, sometimes very violent, consisting of generalized myoclonic jerks without any loss of consciousness or change of colour in the face. The attacks came on sometimes for no apparent reason and sometimes as a result of an injection or a sudden movement. At times the attacks were very frequent. Their intensity varied, but often their duration and violence was such as to require inhalation of *Kélène* to bring the attack to an end—all the sedatives customarily employed being without effect.

In between times the patient received intravenous injections of salicylated iodaseptine (5 ml. every two days). There was no raised temperature, fever manifested only during the period of acute inflammation and rapidly subsided. It was impossible to sit the patient up, and even less feasible to get her up, as the attacks would come on almost at once.

A professor from the Algiers Medical Faculty,[2] who was called into consultation, confirmed the patient's condition without coming to any conclusion as to the nature or cause of the attacks. During his examination he was able to get the patient up. She stayed upright and off the bed for several minutes, but propped up. Examination of the reflexes gave nothing positive. The anti-rheumatic treatment continued.

A few days after the examination by Professor Porrot[2] on July 22nd, 1939, it became possible to get the patient up and even to sit her in an arm chair. The myoclonic attacks appeared to have ceased completely, but it was still impossible to get the patient to walk. The improvement lasted only a short time, and the patient soon took to her bed again. In addition to cervical and lumbar pains, she now complained of a pain situated in the right iliac fossa. This particular symptom had appeared several years previously, simulating appendicitis, for which the patient underwent an operation.

These attacks of pain were very poorly defined and not at all like attacks of renal or gall bladder colic. Examination of the urine has never shown anything abnormal. Palpation of the abdomen revealed a certain degree of distension, but there was no definite sign on which

---

[1] The passage within parentheses is not given in Dr Leuret's book.

[2] In point of fact according to Dr T. Valot (44) the consultant was a psychiatrist, but this pertinent information is withheld.—D.J.W.

to base a diagnosis. The pains occurred frequently and forced the patient to lie in a curled-up position. The myoclonic convulsions completely stopped. This state of affairs persisted for several months, and it remained impossible to get the patient up even during her calm periods.

About this time gastric troubles also appeared, consisting chiefly of hyperchlorhydria and vomiting of food and bile and also very marked anorexia, so much so that feeding was reduced to practically nothing. An X-ray of stomach and gall bladder taken during a calm period revealed nothing. These troubles stopped rather suddenly and were succeeded by poorly defined precordial pains radiating towards the shoulder, not at all like attacks of angina, but sometimes accompanied by dyspnoea.

In the next stage all other symptoms stopped and bladder pains supervened. There was retention of urine necessitating regular catheterization and later a resting catheter, which the patient kept for several months. At the end of that time the catheter was taken away and micturition was normal. During this stage the kidneys had never been enlarged or painful and urine examinations were always negative. This brings us to 1943. The patient's condition was not improving, she was confined to bed and complaining again of excessively violent pains situated as before in the right iliac fossa and in the region of the kidney; but the attacks were now more violent and often necessitated the injection of sedatives. The pain radiated forward under the lower ribs, but never assumed the character of girdle pain. Palpation of the gall bladder caused pain. The digestive troubles became more and more acute; the loss of appetite was almost complete; the patient hardly took any food at all now; wasting was rapid and very considerable; the breath had a strong odour of acetone; the pulse became rapid and the pressure very low. She was given glucose serum and a small dose of insulin to combat the acetosis.

Such was the patient's condition when her family took her away into the interior. Her state was very precarious and a medical man, Dr Pamart of Bel-Abbès, prognosticated an early, fatal outcome.

It was the eve of the Assumption, August 14th, 1943. On the morning of the Festival the patient was transported to the church for Mass. After the Office she expressed a desire to get up, which she did to the great astonishment of those about her. She walked on her own in the church, and she returned on her own to her home, a distance of a hundred metres. She lunched with a big appetite and since then she has experienced no further trouble and has eaten regularly. It would be well, before coming to a definite judgment, to make a detailed analysis of this long history.

There is one indisputable fact, namely the rheumatic attacks revealed by polyarticular inflammations and by the X-rays of cervical, dorsal and lumbar spine (spondylitic lesions with numerous and diffuse vertebral lippings).

The patient's attacks have been very variable in their manifestations. First the generalized myoclonic spasms of the whole body with very powerful muscle jerks. Then come the pains in the right iliac fossa, which appear occasionally, and which towards the end of the illness acquire great violence. Then come the attacks of precordial pain lasting several months and disappearing permanently. Then the urinary retention, necessitating, on two separate occasions, catheterization and a resting catheter for several months. The gastric disturbances must also be mentioned, characterized by a hyperchlorhydria syndrome with vomiting of food and bile; finally the pain in the right hypochondrium, forcing the patient to lie curled up, and the gastric disturbances accompanying an hepatic insufficiency (strong odour of acetone, absolute intolerance of food) which made her condition very alarming.

How to interpret these phenomena? At first sight one cannot discount the possibility of hysterical suggestibility.[1] Myoclonic attacks, appearance and disappearance of pains without apparent cause, their variability; the absence of positive neurological disturbance; the absence of Babinski's sign; the real though transient effect of a strong impression—the examination by the professor from Algiers and his forceful and imperious pronouncements brought about a very big change in the patient's condition, but the effect did not last long. Moreover, it was on this basis[2] that treatment was applied. Two operations were carried out at the patient's request because she believed that the removal of vertebral lippings was possible and would cure her. The result was nil.

In these circumstances, is it not more logical to think of spinal root compression signs at diverse levels of the vertebral column, since the whole of the spine shows pathological signs? In this way a clear and simple explanation could also be found for the visceral manifestations.

In the space of a single day, Mlle Clauzel, who had been in such condition as to cause fear of imminent demise, was able to get up unaided from her stretcher, to walk about in her home without help, no longer suffering, and to eat at table with her relatives. The conclusion, therefore, is that she could not have been cured in such a rapid and complete fashion except by a supernatural manifestation.

*   *   *   *   *

The X-ray reports mentioned by Dr Maurin are not available, but given below are the essentials of a report, dated August 20th, 1945, which is to be found in the dossier at the Lourdes Bureau.

---

[1] *Au premier abord on ne peut s'empêcher de croire à du pithiatisme.*
i.e. the assumption that the symptoms were hysterical.—D.J.W

Radiological Report of Examination of Spinal Column

Cervical Spine: No axial deviation. Profile shows signs of cervical arthritis at C_5, C_6 and C_7 as indicated by:

1. Presence of vertebral lippings anteriorly.
2. Slight permeability of the intervertebral spaces, C_5–C_6 and C_6–C_7 (alteration of the discs).

Dorsal Spine: Slight scoliosis with concavity to the left and torsion of the vertebral axis on itself (deviation to the left of the line of the spinal processes). Localized signs of arthritis at the site of D_8 and D_9; narrowing of the intervertebral spaces, thickening of the surfaces with osteophytic points on their anterior parts (profile view).

Lumbo-sacral Spine: Compensatory lumbar scoliosis towards the right with torsion towards the right of the vertebral axis. Thickening of the articular surfaces of L_1 and L_2.

In its entire extent the density of the vertebral column appears diminished (slight decalcification).

No sacralization, no spina bifida occulta, no spondylolisthesis.

(*Signed*) H. Levrier. August 20th, 1945.

*   *   *   *   *

As a medical document, Dr Maurin's report, like so many of the accounts to be found in the Lourdes files and publications, is curiously imprecise and unsatisfying. Mlle Clauzel had an obscure disorder of many years' duration, yet at no stage does she appear to have had a complete investigation such as would be carried out on a difficult case in any modern hospital. Instead, we are given a catalogue of unexplained symptoms, plus the doctor's guesses as to their possible significance. All one can do, by way of comment, is to add one's own guesses to those of Dr Maurin.

The most obvious feature of the history is the severity and variability of the lady's symptoms in the absence of signs of organic disease sufficient to account for them. Judging by the X-ray report, Mlle Clauzel had arthritis of the spine of simple degenerative type, a common enough condition and by no means enough to account for all her florid symptoms. It is true that when the condition is severe nerve roots may be pressed upon in the region of the spinal foramina, causing pain most noticeable on moving the back, but Dr Maurin's explanation of the whole case in terms of extensive root compression is scarcely plausible. Mlle Clauzel's varied and scattered pains do not conform to the characteristics of root pains, and many of her other symptoms, such as muscle jerkings and inability to eat, bear no relation to root compression. Furthermore, neither the X-ray report quoted above nor the X-ray pictures reproduced in Leuret's book give any support to the assumption of nerve root compression.

If one had available only the story as given in Leuret's book, which does not quote the X-ray findings in detail, one could imagine that Mlle Clauzel was suffering from a more serious complaint, namely ankylosing spondylitis. This form of spinal arthritis leads to extreme rigidity of the back and may produce visceral and girdle pains that simulate renal calculus or pleurisy. It also provokes spasms in the muscles of the back, and it does have periods of acute exacerbation in which the symptoms can be very severe. But Mlle Clauzel's attacks sound highly improbable even for ankylosing spondylitis. Fortunately we have the X-ray report which has been shown to a senior radiologist in a London teaching hospital. The opinion given was that it was a report of a degenerative arthritis with nothing in it to indicate ankylosing spondylitis.

In short, Mlle Clauzel's symptoms seem to be more severe and extraordinary than can be accounted for by the spinal arthritis and postural defect which is all that is indicated in the X-ray report. This points to hysteria, or at least a big hysterical overlay, and this impression is reinforced by the character of the symptoms, muscle jerks, changeable pains and dramatic attacks, which are all typical of hysteria. The terms used by Dr Maurin to describe the pains are in themselves sufficiently revealing: 'poorly defined', 'not at all like angina', 'not girdle pains', 'not like renal or gall-bladder colic'. . . . Furthermore, the sudden suppression of one set of symptoms as another lot appear is typical of an hysterical patient whose attention passes from one locus to another. Hysterical refusal of food and vomiting, with resulting inanition and acetosis is so well known that it has been dignified with a name of its own—anorexia nervosa. It seems only too probable that the later and (from the physical point of view) more serious phase of Mlle Clauzel's disturbance was in fact anorexia nervosa. Indeed, although Dr Maurin does not himself accept this explanation, he gives in his summary a number of weighty reasons for believing in the hysterical nature of most of the symptoms. Several English doctors to whom I have shown Dr Maurin's report all agree that the history suggests hysteria. A psychiatric investigation might have proved the diagnosis, but although Professor Porrot's visit indicates that the need for psychiatric advice was recognized, we are not given any report of his findings.

If the Clauzel case is just another example of hysteria cured dramatically by suggestion, it hardly seems worthwhile to discuss it further. Something can be gained, however, by considering the comments of the Lourdes Bureau and the Canonical Commission. They show how such a simple story can assume the proportions of a miracle cure.

First, the Lourdes Bureau medical notes dated August 19th, 1945.

Lourdes Medical Bureau Report

Mlle Clauzel presented herself on August 19th before the doctors present at the Lourdes Medical Bureau. The report was read from Dr Maurin, in which this colleague describes the illness from which she was cured on August 15th, 1943. According to Dr Maurin it was a question of diffuse rheumatic spondylitis with root compression at diverse levels of the vertebral column. To these compressions were attributed the pains which came on first periodically and, later, constantly and with increasing severity. These pains had had more or less definite connection with many parts of the organism; muscles; cervical, dorsal and lumbar regions; the right iliac fossa; the precordial area; the kidney, bladder, stomach and liver regions; but these pains had been the result of an increasingly severe disturbance of the digestive functions (loss of appetite, absolute intolerance of food, hepatic insufficiency) which reached such a stage that, at the time of her cure, the patient was only expected to live a matter of hours.

Dr Maurin having mentioned in his report the removal of vertebral lippings, Mlle Clauzel was examined and three median scars were noted at the site of the spinal processes of the lower cervical, mid-dorsal and first lumbar vertebrae.

The region of the vertebral column is over its whole extent completely insensitive to percussion, and lateral movements and extension and flexion movements are quite free from pain.

(Dr Maurin having mentioned the possibility of hysterical suggestibility, a colleague took the opportunity when her chest was exposed to make a series of pricks with a pin over the arms, shoulder and back, asking the patient to answer yes or no. It did not seem that there was any diminution of sensibility, the responses being on the whole satisfactory, no zone of insensibility being revealed. Besides, Mlle Clauzel was known to one of our colleagues for more than twenty years. He can testify to the simplicity of her character, and to the fact that she is not subject to exaltation of any kind and is incapable of changing the truth for any purpose whatsoever.

A slight scoliosis is to be noted, with concavity to the left, and a slight kyphosis of the dorsal region. . . .

Now, according to the X-rays, the osseous new-growths, cause of the irritation of the nerve roots, are unchanged. One might put this case among those exceptional Lourdes cures in which the functional cure precedes or takes the place of the organic cure.

Dr Pellissier, who was still present at Lourdes on September 11th, told us that having encountered Mlle Clauzel several times in the street he noted, and we are entirely of the same opinion, a change for the better in the patient's vertebral stature, which was very apparent as regards the attitude of scoliosis. The back is in some measure straighter, the gait more assured).[1]

The Lourdes Bureau's notes cast no further light on the nature of the illness, but they reveal an attitude of mind in the doctors responsible, who seem determined at all costs to avoid the obvious natural explanation. The fact that the X-ray showed no change in the arthritic spine after the symptoms had suddenly disappeared would suggest to the ordinary person that the symptoms were not due to the physical state, and that their disappearance was due to some mental change not registered on an X-ray. The Lourdes Bureau notes completely overlook this straightforward explanation, and instead put forward the curious view that the miracle consisted in the organic condition being prevented from continuing to produce its customary symptomatic effects.

There are also other curious arguments. The variability of the symptoms and the severity of the illness are blithely attributed to 'increasingly severe disturbance of the digestive func-

---

[1] The section of the report within parentheses, separately dated September 12th, 1945, is not included in the report as quoted in *Guérisons Miraculeuses Modernes*.

tions'. Considering the diagnosis was spinal arthritis, this explanation is—to put it mildly—inadequate. There is also the naïve implied assumption that because one of the doctors did not discover zones of anaesthesia on the skin (such as sometimes appear in gross hysteria) this can be taken as evidence of the non-hysterical nature of the illness.

The actual circumstances of the cure, and further comments on its supposedly miraculous character, are given in the report of the Canonical Commission of Inquiry appointed by the Bishop of Oran 'for the purpose of judging the supernatural character of Mlle Gabrielle Clauzel's cure'. The Commission's report begins with a reiteration of the history of the illness:

Report of the Commission of Inquiry

Excellency,

By a Decree, of February 11th, 1948, Your Excellency, at the request of Dr Vallet, President of the Lourdes Medical Bureau, appointed a Commission composed of the undersigned, and charged them to inquire into the cure of Mlle Gabrielle Clauzel, President of the 'Society of Friends of Our Lady of Lourdes in Oran', who lives at Oran, 20 rue d'Alsace-Lorraine.

The purpose of the inquiry was to determine whether the cure which took place on August 15th, 1943, should be attributed to the intervention of Our Lady of Lourdes. The said Commission, having terminated its inquiry, has the honour to submit for Your Excellency's approval the results of their labours and the conclusions which, in their opinion, derive therefrom.

The inquiry was carried out under three headings:

1. The occurrence of the cure, from the account of the beneficiary herself and the attendant witnesses.
2. The medical notes on the said occurrence.
3. The extraordinary features which call attention to this cure.

The present report expounds successively the results of the inquiry on these three points and the conclusion which, in the opinion of the Commission, appears to derive therefore:

I. *The Illness and the Cure.* (i) *The Illness*

From Mlle Gabriel Clauzel's account of her illness, or rather the consequences of the development of her illness—because it does not seem to be this same condition which led her to the gates of the tomb—begins in June, 1936 with an abscess originating from a haemorrhoid, necessitating a stay in hospital from June 20th to August 7th.

4

She goes to Lourdes on August 10th with the pilgrimage from Oran. In the meantime a recto-vaginal fistulous track forms, for which she has an operation in October of the same year, 1936. Recurrences and further operations in February, April and November, 1937. It was at this time there appeared the 'first attack of rheumatoid arthritis at the site of the left wrist, which is very swollen and very painful'.

It was the first manifestion of the illness the cure of which provides the subject of the present examination. This does not mean to say, however, as Dr Vallet himself pointed out in his report, that the disease had not already been present in the organism for some time, but this was its first open manifestation. This attack lasted two months. The articulations of the cervical column were also very painful. In March, 1938, following some ill-defined pains in the right iliac fossa, Mlle Clauzel underwent an appendicectomy operation. These pains re-appeared again in a more intense form, which led to the presumption that, like all the other disturbances, they were the consequence of vertebral rheumatism. Recovery was very slow after each surgical operation. After the last operation, there was great difficulty in walking. The upright position was distressing; the body bent forward, even the sitting position was tiring. She could not straighten her neck and the head stayed sunk on the front of the neck. 'I seemed to crawl rather than to walk,' said Mlle Clauzel.

On January 2nd, 1939, 'while making a bed,' Mlle Clauzel experienced a further attack. She was stricken with violent lumbar pains and could not straighten herself up. At first lumbago was thought of, but the pain increased and soon extended the whole length of the spine; cervical, dorsal and lumbar.

She had a further stay in hospital from January 20th to August 3rd. Following an X-ray on March 1st, 1939, a firm diagnosis of vertebral rheumatism was made. In January, a professor from Algiers, Dr Porrot, called into consultation, maintained, or rather did not contradict, the firm diagnosis of her own doctor. With the fine weather came a slight improvement. Mlle Clauzel was able to go on the pilgrimage to Lourdes (August); she could maintain a sitting position, but she could not walk on her own. As in previous years, she was sufficiently determined to take several baths in the pool; this year she took five. In addition, she attended the various pilgrimage ceremonies in a small motor from the 'Hospitalité', because she could not move around otherwise. She felt a slight improvement, which kept up during a short stay at Aix-les-Bains—interrupted by the general mobilization. She left hurriedly to get back to Algeria. Held up at Montpellier, she could not embark until September 22nd. The improvement was maintained. When she visited her doctor in Oran, he told her: 'Be careful when the weather begins to change; you are not cured.' She was quite disappointed, but in fact the improvement kept up until the end of the year. She was able to attend to her work.

The doctor was right: in January, 1940, Mlle Clauzel had a relapse which lasted until June of the same year. In June, as each year, there was a slight improvement which, on this occasion, lasted until November 15th.

During this period Mlle Clauzel followed the classic treatment for rheumatism; regular ingestion of salicylate by mouth and intravenous injections of iodaseptine. On November 15th, 1940, after a further attack more violent than the others, Mlle Clauzel took to her bed to leave it no more. The illness assumed a very serious character. The patient was no longer capable of raising herself in bed and the least movement caused unspeakable suffering. The chief organs were affected, one·after the other. On two occasions, in August, 1942, and in February, 1943, retention of urine forced her to have a permanent catheter for several months. Then it was the liver and the intestines which were affected. At the same time she had continual head pains and precordial pains; her eyes tolerated daylight very badly. Nevertheless, in her calmer periods, Mlle Clauzel continued to concern herself with 'The Society of Friends of Our Lady of Lourdes', of which she was still President. Her family regarded this activity disapprovingly, but, with the support of her doctor, who rightly viewed this as a distraction from her trouble, she continued. In 1941, thinking that with the removal of several vertebral lippings, visible on the X-ray, she would be cured, she asked her doctor if he would do this operation. For a long time he refused, but in October he carried it out, seemingly with the idea of influencing her morale. The result was nil. In May, 1942, she took part, on a stretcher, in a pilgrimage to the Grotto of Misserghin. In spite of the consolation and joy which she derived from this, she acknowledged that the journey was very painful. Further ablation of bony lippings in June, 1943, produced no result. In fact, during this time the illness continued to get worse. From the beginning of 1943 onwards Mlle Clauzel lost a great deal of weight and by June the wasting was frightful. The patient felt that this time, 'she would have difficulty in making up lost ground'. As we have said, Mlle Clauzel still concerned herself with the 'Society of Friends of Our Lady of Lourdes', but, strangely, she had never dreamed of asking for her own cure; it was asked on/her behalf, but she herself did not think of it. She said: 'I knew very well that Our Lady of Lourdes could do anything, but so many other favours seemed to me more necessary than my cure, that I preferred to ask for everything else but my own recovery.' At the end of July, 1943, her family wanted to take Mlle Clauzel to the country, at Pallisy. Her state of health prevented it, and the journey had to be postponed for a week. At that time she was having intractable vomiting, and could not tolerate the smallest amount of food. She had a crisis of acidosis. The acetonaemia was intense, the odour of the breath very strong to the point of inconvenience. The pulse was fast and poor, and it was feared the end was near. She could not be moved until August 6th. The week that followed was wretched. Mlle Clauzel wanted to be weighed. Fully dressed she

weighed thirty-five kilos. On August 11th Dr Pamart, from Sidi Bel-
Abbès, pronounced that Mlle Clauzel was in the last extremity. But
August 15th arrived, the greatest festival of the Holy Virgin, anni-
versary of the Pilgrimage to Lourdes, to the organization of which
Mlle Clauzel was still devoted: it was besides her own birthday. On
this occasion a novena was offered to the Holy Virgin. In addition,
Monseigneur at Oran, and M. l'Abbé Capparos at Santa Cruz, were
saying Mass for her. For all these reasons, but without thinking explicitly about her cure, she insisted on attending the Mass at her
parish church. 'I really thought that this Mass would be my last, and
that soon I would have to leave everything.' Her wish was thought to
be unreasonable, but as it was probably the last one that could be
satisfied she was taken on a stretcher to the parish church close by.

The Cure

As for the cure, Mlle Clauzel's testimony is very succinct. She tells
us simply: 'What happened then (that is to say during the Mass) I
can hardly comprehend myself even now, all my miseries disappeared
in an instant.' Mlle Dufour, who testified before the Lourdes Medical
Bureau, gives us some further details. Says Mlle Dufour: 'On the
morning of August 15th, when Mlle Clauzel was at her last extremity,
she had herself carried to the parish church on a stretcher. Her request
was acceded to thinking that it would be her last, but it was considered
quite unreasonable.'

She was taken to the church an hour before the ceremony, which was
furthermore delayed by the confession of Italian prisoners. The
ceremony lasted one-and-a-half hours. Obviously it was rather long for
someone in Mlle Clauzel's condition. During the Mass, and especially
between the Elevation and the Communion, Mlle Clauzel gave signs
of agitation to which those about her were not accustomed. Naturally
they were anxious, thinking that she was exhausted by the length of
the ceremony. 'In reality,' said Mlle Dufour, 'it was her cure, the
effects of which she was feeling without being able to believe what had
happened, considering herself unworthy of such a favour.' She recited
the Communion; she wanted very much to get up, but waited until the
end of the Mass to act upon her wish. At the end of the Mass, still
controlled by a certain doubt, or a certain modesty, she waited until
there were hardly any witnesses. Then, she wanted to put her feet to
the ground. People discouraged her for fear of the consequences. She
insisted, 'raised herself up on her stretcher, which she hadn't done for
years, let herself down, and walked to the altar and back without any
kind of help.' She said that it seemed to her she wasn't touching the
ground. She was made to get back on the stretcher, however, in order
to return home. But at home, she wanted to get up, and had a large
basin of *café au lait* with some slices of bread and butter, without being
deterred from taking a cup of milk a little later. At the midday meal,
which the family wanted to be something plain, she insisted, on account

of the clear signs of cure, on tasting everything—olives, ham, *pâté*, two helpings of fried potatoes, three cutlets, a slice of cake. 'This meal, which would have suffocated anyone who had fasted for a long time, was followed by an evening meal with vegetable soup and some cutlets.'

This instantaneous cure established itself and was maintained. Mlle Clauzel gained weight: 1.500 kg. weekly, until she had reached 57 or 58 kilos. Her strength returned rapidly. Her movements and her strength astonished her entourage. Ten months later, during a long procession at the Fête-Dieu, she carried the heavy banner of the Children of Mary. On August 15th, 1944, a year after her cure, she took charge of one of the bearing poles of the stand supporting the heavy statue of the Virgin. There is no form of work that frightens her. Every morning she helps at a busy clinic in Oran. Twice she has given her blood for urgent transfusions. Among those who know her and see her often, Mlle Clauzel enjoys a reputation for good sense, sound judgment and staunch piety, which is confirmed by her depositions and by her modest bearing, reserved, and full of tact, during the inquiry of the Lourdes Medical Bureau. In addition, in order to confirm the evidence given the following have been heard:

1. Sister Adèle, of the Sisters of the Trinity, living at Oran, who testified to Mlle Clauzel's desperate condition when she left for Palissy.

2. Dr Zimmermann, of Sidi Bel-Abbès, who testified to Mlle Clauzel's lamentable condition when she arrived at Pallisy.

3. Madame Caizergues, sister of Mlle Clauzel, with whom the sick woman stayed, who testified to her desperate state and to the accuracy of the details of the cure reported by Mlles Dufour and Clauzel.

4. Canon Capparos, Vicar of Perregaux and Chaplain to the Society of 'Friends of Our Lady of Lourdes' in Oran, who testified to Mlle Clauzel's desperate state, for the cure of which he celebrated Mass in the Chapel of Santa Cruz on the morning of August 15th, 1943, and exhorted members of the Society to pray. He testified also to Mlle Clauzel's calm and stable mentality and to her profound piety.

From what has been stated it is clear that Mlle Clauzel, who had been suffering for at least six years from a very serious illness, who had been bedridden for three years, and who, in the third week of August, 1943, had reached the last extremity, was cured instantaneously, without the aid of any remedy, on August 15th, 1943, and her cure is maintained to this day.

The ex-patient, her relatives, her friends and her companions from the Society, 'The Friends of Our Lady of Lourdes', all consider that this cure, under the circumstances in which it was produced, is a real miracle.

There is little to be said about this more detailed represen-
tation of the history save that it is cast in such a way as to high-
light the dramatic change in the patient's condition and to gloss
over the absence of any clear evidence as to the organic basis
of her illness. The Commission appears to attach considerable
weight to the testimony of lay witnesses present during those
dramatic moments after the criticial Mass when the bedridden
woman was seen to get up from her stretcher and walk around.
From the scientific standpoint that is not the essential feature
of the case. It cannot too often be stressed that, in order to
establish that a real organic change has taken place, there must
be a change observable by X-rays or laboratory tests, or at least
a definite change in the clinical signs (e.g. reflexes, measurements, chest sounds, etc.) elicited by skilled medical examination. In the absence of such objective evidence, no amount of
change in the patient's feelings, attitude or behaviour, however
dramatic it may appear to the onlooker, is sufficient to provide
scientific proof of an organic cure. The most frightful limps
and contortions, the most crippling paralyses, if they are of
hysterical origin, are sometimes relieved instantaneously by
psychological influences. It is a common enough experience
in mental hospitals for stuporose patients, who have refused to
get up for months on end and have had to be forcibly fed through
a stomach tube, suddenly to start moving around and eating
again. They do so in response to some inner mental impulse
which in no way signifies an organic change. Even patients
with serious organic disorders can be made suddenly to change
their behaviour. The sufferings of dying cancer patients have
been relieved most dramatically in certain cases by the use of
hypnotism, but there is no question of a 'cure' or a 'miracle'
having taken place.

The next section of the Commission's report deals with
Dr Maurin's account and with the Lourdes Bureau notes. As
both of these have been reproduced and commented upon
already we can pass on to Section III, which contains the Commission's comments:

III. *The Extraordinary Characteristics of the Cure*

Following the account which she has herself given, and following the notes and conclusions of her own doctor and of the medical experts at the Lourdes Medical Bureau, Mlle Clauzel's cure demands attention on account of several extraordinary features which, in the doctors' opinions, place the case above or outside natural laws. Herewith the said features:

1. Absence of any special medication that could explain the recovery.
2. Instantaneousness of the cure.
3. Absence of any convalescent period.
4. Persistence of the organic cause which, according to her own doctor and the medical experts, accounted for the functional troubles.
5. Various other circumstances associated with the cure.

1. *Absence of any specific medication*

In the course of the six long years her illness lasted, Mlle Clauzel followed all kinds of treatments: surgical, pharmaceutical, and even psychological. All proved ineffective. The illness followed its fatal course up to the point of death. When in the opinions of the doctors, the people around about her and Mlle Clauzel herself, death was imminent, then the cure took place, no treatment being given at the time, the situation being considered hopeless.

2. *Instantaneousness of the Cure*

This is one of the chief features of Mlle Clauzel's case, one which already indicates the operation of a supernatural agency. Mlle G. Clauzel, as we have seen, had suffered from a whole series of functional disturbances in the course of six long years, which were all the time becoming more frequent and more serious, until she reached the final extremity. On the eve of her cure she was in such a state that 'it was feared the end was near' (Dr Maurin); on August 11th, Dr Pamart of Sidi Bel-Abbès pronounced the same opinion. It was also her own opinion: 'I thought that this would be my last Mass and that soon I would have to leave everything.' It was also the opinion of those close to her. She wanted to hear a last Mass, because she had not had this consolation since the beginning of her illness. Her wish was acceded to, although it seemed unreasonable, because it was 'thought that it was her last' (Mlle Dufour).

She was carried to church on a stretcher. Between the Elevation and the Communion, she showed signs of agitation to which those about her were not accustomed. They were anxious because they thought she was tired by the lengthy ceremony. In reality it was the cure which was taking effect. She communicated on her stretcher. At the conclusion of the Mass, in spite of the opposition of those present, she wanted to get up and she slid down from her stretcher. She reached the altar without help, and for the rest of the day walked about like a normal person.

How to explain this strength and this mobility in the limbs of someone who, an hour before, and for months, had scarcely been able to tolerate any other position than lying curled up? After Mass she consumed a large basin of *café au lait* with bread and butter. At the midday meal she had 'olives, ham, *pâté*, two helpings of fried potatoes, three cutlets, a slice of cake', and in the evening vegetable soup and more cutlets. How to explain this diet which should have suffocated a person condemned for so long to absolute fasting, a diet which was not merely tolerated, but desired and perfectly digested by a person in whom, on the days before, and for a long time, there had been an absolute anorexia and intolerance of all food (Dr Maurin), with hyperchlorhydria, vomiting of food and bile, hepatic insufficiency (strong odour of acetone) (Dr Maurin)? All the digestive disturbance from which Mlle Clauzel was suffering, and all the pains which she was enduring disappeared at the same time and with the same suddenness. Mlle Clauzel has henceforth led the normal life of a healthy, active individual. She takes part every day in the exacting work of a private clinic. Twice she has given her blood for urgent transfusions. One cannot discover a natural explanation for this sudden recovery.

3. *Absence of a period of Convalescence*

Mlle Clauzel, who in the morning of August 15th was still in a desperate state, in the evening of August 15th, and in the days that followed, gave the impression of a person in perfect health. The diet which she took, after an absolute anorexia and intolerance of all food, is testimony to that.

The fact that she gained progressively 23 kg., 1½ kg. per week, more than what could properly be called a manifestation of convalescence, must, in the present instance, be considered as a sign and a test of the perfect cure of the functional disturbance of the organs which were, at this stage, the ones most affected (stomach, liver). Thus it must be stated that Mlle Clauzel's cure took place without any period of convalescence, which is against all the laws of nature. There was no intermediate stage between illness and perfect health.

4. *Persistence of the Organic Cause of the Illness*

The objection might, perhaps, be made that Mlle Clauzel's cure, which seemingly consisted chiefly of recovery of multiple functions, could be placed in the category of so-called functional cures and, as such, might not be considered because of the close dependence of these illnesses on the nervous system, a dependence which renders them particularly liable to the influence of auto-or hetero-suggestion. It must be noted that the disease from which Mlle Clauzel suffered is an organic ailment (rheumatic spondylitis with compression of the nerve roots) which, like all organic diseases, brings about more or less serious functional troubles—very serious in the present case since they brought the patient to the gates of the tomb.

Now the functional troubles have been cured 'according to the evidence of the X-ray of August 29th, 1945, without the organic condition having been cured' (vertebral deformation, osteophytes) which, according to the experts, was the cause of them. In our opinion, this consideration, far from detracting from the importance of the cure, doubles the marvel, in a case in which the dependence of the organic condition and the functional disturbance is well established. Now, all the medical experts have pronounced upon the very close dependence which exists between the organic condition and the functional disturbances (the twelve doctors who signed the Lourdes Medical Bureau certificate, and also the patient's doctor, Dr Maurin). As for the cure having been of a functional kind, perhaps caused by auto- or hetero-suggestion, this seems to have no applicability to Mlle Clauzel's case. She herself avows that she never solicited her cure, finding that she had a thousand more pressing things to ask for. Besides, her general attitude in life, and during the inquiry at Lourdes and at Oran, shows her to be a person possessed of simplicity of character, sound, practical good sense, integrity above all suspicion, and deep and serious piety.

5. Other Remarkable Circumstances

The diverse circumstances which mark this cure that cannot be explained by material causes indicate in what direction its origin is to be sought. In the first place, the beneficiary's character—President of the Society of 'Friends of Our Lady of Lourdes in Oran'—her devotion to Our Lady of Lourdes, her zeal for propagating devotion to the Virgin of the Grotto, in particular her zeal for organizing the pilgrimages of August 15th to Lourdes; in the second place the coincidence between the cure and the Masses and prayers that on August 15th were imploring Heaven for the favour of a miraculous intervention; the fact that on her own avowal she had not asked for a cure; all these circumstances only make the hypothesis of auto- or hetero-suggestion more improbable.

The Commission of Inquiry's Conclusion

Mlle Clauzel's case, with the extraordinary features enumerated above, is one of those exceptional, scientifically inexplicable events in the face of which one naturally thinks of a supernatural intervention. In consequence of which:

Given the account of the cure by the beneficiary herself with all the guarantees of sincerity that could be desired, and the attestations of well-informed and serious witnesses;

Given the circumstances and the conclusions expounded in

Dr Maurin's handwriting in the complementary certificate of August 24th, 1945, ending by recognizing the fact of the instantaneousness of the cure and its inexplicability by natural causes;

Given that the same circumstances have been subscribed to and signed by twelve doctors met to examine the case under the chairmanship of Dr Vallet at the Lourdes Medical Bureau on September 12th, 1945;

Given the characteristics which mark this cure, namely the instantaneous, complete and permanent disappearance of an extremely serious functional illness, without any material curative agent, without any period of convalescence and without the removal of the organic deformation which was the natural cause of the illness—as attested by scientific men of incontestable worth and authority—which is a sure sign of a supernatural intervention;

Given the connection which exists between the occasion of the cure and the prayers addressed to Our Lady of Lourdes for the beneficiary's cure;

The Commission of Inquiry, convoked by Your Excellency, having most carefully considered, and called upon the Holy Name of God, declare:

1. That they consider certain the fact of Mlle Clauzel's instantaneous cure without the intervention of any material agent, and without any period of convalescence, and this in spite of the persistence of the organic causes of the illness.

2. That this cure should be attributed to a special intervention of God obtained through the intercession of Our Lady of Lourdes.

3. That, in consequence, in the unanimous opinion of the Commission, Your Excellency may safely pronounce as to the miraculous character of the said cure.

Oran, March 18th, 1948.

(Report signed by the five members of the Commission, Canon Carmouye, Canon Domas, M. Henri, M. Manières and M. l'Abbé Collet.)

Although the comments in the Canonical Commission's report are so repetitious, I have reproduced them in full in this one case in order to convey the nature and quality of the arguments which appear in these documents. This instance is typical. The ecclesiastics' own particular interpretation of the evidence is reiterated again and again with no consideration of alternative possibilities. The ecclesiastical criteria of instantaneousness of recovery, absence of convalescent period, absence of medication and so forth, have but slight relevance to the scientific question of whether an unexplained organic change took place. Lay observation as to the lady's spirited character and pious nature are no contra-indication whatsoever to the hypothesis that her functional disturbance was largely psychogenic.

One point which deserves consideration is the remarkable facility with which Mlle Clauzel walked and ate in spite of being bedridden and starving for a long period. Even a constitutionally perfectly healthy person, if he is laid flat for months, cannot regain the use of his legs immediately on getting up; and a person who has starved for a long period cannot immediately digest a large meal. On the other hand, hysterical disabilities are notoriously inconstant. A paralysis that appears complete when a group of persons gather round to examine it may disappear when the patient is alone and occupied with other thoughts. In a case of hysteria with apparently complete loss of power to walk or to eat the patient would have to be submitted to prolonged and vigilant scrutiny in hospital before one could feel confident that her disability was really constant and absolute.

The impressive and assertive language used in the Commission's report might well lead a lay person to a completely false picture of the facts and their various possible interpretations. For instance, the statement that during six years all kinds of treatments were followed conceals the fact that, except for anti-rheumatic therapy, no specific treatment was given because no specific disease was diagnosed. The statement that her rapid increase in weight following the miracle can be considered as a sign of cure of her stomach and liver disorder conceals the fact that there is no evidence of specific stomach or liver disorder other than what would result from not eating. I have already remarked upon the curious twisted argument according to which persistence of the arthritic state of the spine is supposed to make the miracle all the more remarkable. The statement that Mlle Clauzel suffered from an organic ailment which brings about more or less serious functional trouble conceals the enormous discrepancy between the benign nature of her spinal arthritis and the extreme severity of her symptoms. No psychiatrically orientated medical man could follow the Commission's line of reasoning according to which the in-

fluence of suggestion is ruled out by the patient's denial that
she had personally solicited her own cure. The very coincidence between the cure and the triple occasion of the Mass,
the birthday and the prayers being said for her, which appears
to impress the Commission, serves only to increase the likelihood of influence by suggestion.

The Canonical Commission cannot be held entirely responsible for making unjustifiable assertions, for they are based in
large part on the technical advice of the doctors of the Lourdes
Bureau. In this case Dr Vallet and his colleagues who signed
the report are the real originators of the dogmatic declarations.
Dr Maurin at least considered other interpretations, even
though he did not appear to agree with them. It seems to me
that in this and in many other instances the Lourdes Bureau
has lent its support to cures without sufficiently investigating
the case and without giving fair consideration to interpretations
that do not fit in with the idea of a miracle.

Another point to notice is that strictly speaking this was not
a cure at Lourdes at all, since the cure took place in Algiers
after prayers had been said. By including cures from elsewhere
among their records the Lourdes Bureau greatly increase the
chances of selecting spontaneous recoveries with only coin-
cidental connection with the supposed power associated with
Lourdes. Another instance of this kind is the cure of Sister
Marie Marguerite, which is described later, and which is
another of the official miracles. That cure took place in a convent without the sick patient making a pilgrimage, although
Lourdes water was administered. In this report I have included
those cures from elsewhere which form part of the Lourdes
Bureau records and have been declared miraculous, but I have
not considered other cures that have been accepted as miraculous by the Sacred Congregation of Rites—e.g. the cures of
Sister Mary Teresa (Moran) in 1946 and Sister Brendan in
1942, with diagnoses of disseminated sclerosis and Pott's disease respectively, which were referred to in The Tablet, May
19th, 1956.

2. MME GESTAS

This lady visited Lourdes for the first time in August, 1946. She was then aged 49 and was suffering from abdominal pains and digestive troubles consequent upon a partial gastrectomy operation carried out for the relief of stomach ulcer. She returned home feeling no different. Her doctor thought she was improved, but she was certainly far from well. She visited Lourdes again in August, 1947, and this time she experienced a swift and complete relief from all her symptoms. Ultimately the Archbishop of Bordeaux declared her cure miraculous.

On the form provided for those taking part in organized pilgrimages Mme Gestas submitted the following medical certificate from her surgeon:

Copy of Medical Certificate
  by Dr G. Dubourg, 26 Allées d'Amour, Bordeaux.

I the undersigned Dr Dubourg declare that Mme Gestas has had operations on three occasions since Xmas, 1943.

1st operation (Xmas, 1943). Gastrectomy for callous ulcer of the lesser curvature.

2nd operation (May, 1944). Surgical treatment of a small diaphragmatic hernia of the great tuberosity of the stomach through the oesophagal orifice of the diaphragm. A colectomy was carried out during this operation at the situation of the transverse part for inflammatory pericolitis.

3rd operation (January 1946). Liberation of adhesions. Since then Mme Gestas has been the victim of dyspeptic attacks with vomiting and pseudo-ulcer pains, and of attacks of partial intestinal obstruction. On the whole a significant improvement of the various disturbances which she experiences must be noted. The pains are less intense, the vomitings have almost ceased. The acute attacks of intestinal obstruction are less frequent.

But there are still recurrences of the painful syndrome which indicate the existence of an adhesive peritonitis at the sub-umbilical level. The general state, although improved, is still poor.

(Signed) G. Dubourg.[1]

Further symptoms attributed to Mme Gestas during the period 1946–47 were:

[1] Undated, but presumably July, 1947.—D.J.W.

'Neuro-vegetative dystonia: frequent fainting, always after meals. Vertigo in the streets when vehicles or bicycles pass by, and even without apparent reason.' (These details are given by Dr Bourg on the Lourdes Bureau examination form dated April, 1948.)

On her first visit, Mme Gestas, who professed to have little faith in the likelihood of cure, submitted herself to no more than an anointing with water from the healing pool, and returned home, according to her own account, not at all improved. During her second visit, on August 22nd, 1947, she actually immersed herself in the waters, and felt a pulling sensation in her abdomen. Later in the day she noticed an improvement in her symptoms. The next day she felt completely fit and ate some haricot beans, digesting them without pain. From that time on she remained perfectly fit and soon regained the weight she had lost during her illness.

Some further details are given in a certificate from Dr R. J. George, the patient's general practitioner:

Dr R. J. George. Certificate. 5th December, 1947.

I the undersigned doctor of medicine certify that I have looked after Mme Gestas, residing at Rue Camille Duluc, Begles, since 1943.

In October, 1943 Mme Gestas had gastric disturbances. Radiological examination revealed an ulcer of the lesser curvature.

In the face of the failure of medical treatment, gastrectomy was decided upon and carried out on December 29th, 1943 by Dr G. Dubourg. It did not lead to a disappearance of the painful element.

A radiological examination by Professor Dubarry in March, 1944, revealed the existence of a diaphragmatic hernia containing a part of the stomach.

This was operated upon on May 11th, 1944. After the operation there was a considerable peritoneal reaction necessitating application of ice to the abdomen for eighteen days.

On account of the persisting pains a further X-ray was taken in November, 1945 which revealed another diaphragmatic hernia. The patient asked for a further operation, which took place on January 4th, 1946. The whole epigastric region was found to be invaded by a tight web of adhesions which, on incision, concealed the abdominal organs, thus prolonging the operation and bringing about dramatic after effects: (1° Prolonged state of shock—pulmonary congestion; 2° Fistula of the abdominal wall).

Since her return home on February 17th, 1946 until August 27th, 1947, Mme Gestas did not cease to suffer and had several attacks of partial intestinal obstruction, one of which, on May 2nd, 1946, necessitated continuous aspiration for forty-eight hours.

I have seen Mme Gestas again on September 3rd, 1947; she is completely transformed, she suffers no longer and has regained her good general condition.

(Signed) Dr George

Dr Dubourg and Dr George both re-examined the patient on separate occasions during 1948 and testified to her continued sound state of health.

The medical information so far is imprecise and scanty, quite insufficient to provide a basis for an independent opinion as to the seriousness or otherwise of the patient's condition. Her original complaint, gastric ulcer, had been treated surgically, and her continued troubles were presumably due to the complications of surgery. Fibrous adhesions due to inflammation at the site of an operation can certainly produce a great deal of pain and digestive disturbance, but they are notoriously variable in their effects, and many patients come to terms with their adhesions in the course of time and live without much disturbance. The dizziness and the fainting attacks after meals are indications of dumping syndrome, a well-known complication of gastrectomy operation. It is due to a too rapid passage of food from the remnant of stomach to the commencement of the small intestine which, by bringing about sudden intestinal dilatation, produces the characteristic symptoms. The important point is that the syndrome is often self-limiting, and one expects the symptoms to improve with time.

It appears that Mme Gestas was not suffering from any specific disease that would be expected to lead to death or disablement, and that her disturbances were of such a nature as might well improve of their own accord. Dr Dubourg's opinion that there was an improvement following her first Lourdes visit strongly suggests that her disturbance was already on the mend some time before the date of the supposed miracle.

Fortunately, in this case there is available one medical document that is both detailed and objective—a refreshing change from the mass of Lourdes material. This is an X-ray report dated November 17th, 1945. It confirms that Mme Gestas suffered from a dumping syndrome, and it reveals no sign of other organic disease. The only other remarkable feature is the presence of the transverse colon said to have been removed the previous year by Dr Dubourg. Possibly only a very small section was removed, too small to be obvious in the X-ray, but discrepancies of this kind, passed over without comment, cast doubt upon the scientific seriousness of the Lourdes documents and provide a further indication of the superficial way in which the cases have been investigated. The X-ray report reads as follows:

Result of Radiological Examination of Mme Gestas.
(*Carried out November 17th, 1945.*)

Lungs: No pathological signs.
Heart Aorta: Diameters in conformity with the patient's build.
Liver: Volume normal. No abnormal appearance to be seen in the situation of the hepatic parenchyma or the gall-bladder. This latter is not clearly sensitive to deep pressure.
Oesophagus. Normal transit.

In the sub-diaphragmatic region there is rather persistently to be observed a very very small and slightly atypical hernia of the great gastric tuberosity, through the oesophageal opening, which is particularly evident, of course, in dorsal decubitus, but which is also visible in the form of gaseous bubble on certain films taken in the standing position.

Stomach. Films have been taken at short intervals during the different stages of passing down because, contrary to what one might think clinically, the stoma functions very rapidly and even to the point of being incontinent.

The gastrectomy has been very radical. At the site of the gastric stump, slight hypertrophy of the folds of the gastric mucosa following the surgical interventions.

Slight aerophagia.

No abnormal appearance in the region of the orifice or the efferent loop, but during the excessively rapid emptying of the gastric contents, which we have already noted, the jejunal loops dilate. They are supple, mobile, non-painful.

The patient is seen again $8\frac{1}{4}$ hours after taking the opaque meal. The stomach and the loops of the small intestine are empty, save for a terminal 50 cm. of ileum, which are still injected.

The colon is filled from the caecum to the splenic angle. The mobility of the transverse colon, which is spastic and situated high up, is diminished, as often happens after gastrectomy. Its middle portion is sensitive to deep pressure, but it is difficult to say whether it is not actually a pain due to the scar.

In order to reveal completely the colonic field an opaque enema was administered which showed nothing beyond the points already noted except for a clear elongation of the sigmoid amounting almost to a dolichosigmoid appearance.

In summary:

From the radiological point of view this patient has:

Incontinence of the gastro-enterostomy orifice with very rapid passage in the jejunal loops, which dilate.

No apparent anomaly from the morphological standpoint of the orifice or the efferent loop.

Small hernia through the oesophageal hiatus with slight aerophagia.

Transverse colon situated high up and of diminished mobility.

Dolichosigmoid.

Dr Roger Guichard

Bordeaux.

The discussions on this cure included some mention of a nervous element. Probably there was, for gastric ulcer often occurs in association with neurotic conflict, and Mme Gestas' 'dizziness when vehicles pass by' does not sound like a purely organically determined symptom. In any case, sudden relief from symptoms under the influence of a powerful suggestion requires no particular explanation when the organic disturbance underlying them is anyway on the mend. Even in persons not ordinarily neurotic, symptoms often continue after the physical disturbance has subsided. After all the operations and complications Mme Gestas underwent, she would be a stoic indeed not to have developed some nervous overlay.

To conclude, this case appears so unimpressive one wonders how Professor Pierre Mauriac could describe it as 'inexplicable', how the National Committee of doctors could unanimously agree with him and finally how the Archbishop's Commission could pass it as miraculous. The fact that a case with such obvious possibilities for ordinary explanations could get by all these authorities suggests that once a miraculous interpretation has been authoritatively stated other explanations receive scant consideration.

3. MME ROSE MARTIN

This is the only one of the recent miracle cases that purports to be a cancer cure. The following facts about her medical history are all that are given in the dossier. They are written (apparently subsequently to her cure) on the case-record form of the Hôpital Pasteur, Nice, where the patient was treated, and are signed by her surgeon, Dr Fay.

In November, 1945, at the age of 44, Mme Martin began to suffer from loss of blood following sexual intercourse. On vaginal examination the cervix was indurated, presenting a woody hardness, and bled at the slightest touch. Her uterus was removed by Dr. Barraya on February 19th, 1946 (radical hysterectomy, Wertheim technique) and microscopic examination of the cervix confirmed the diagnosis of adeno-carcinoma.

It is also recorded that she had a harsh second heart sound audible at the base and that her aorta, on X-ray screening, was seen to be enlarged. The subsequent progress of this abnormality receives no mention.

Five days after her operation the abdominal wound broke open and a strangulating abdominal hernia formed. ('Désunion de la paroi avec sphacèle éviscération.') Her general condition was very poor. On October 4th, 1946, she had a further operation to remedy the abdominal hernia and to close an abdominal fistula.

Six months after this, on April 25th, 1947, she returned complaining of attacks of pain in the rectum and radiating to the legs. It was impossible for her to empty the bowel without the aid of an enema. On rectal palpation a swelling the size of a mandarine was felt in the anterior wall of the rectum at the recto-sigmoid junction. The swelling could also be felt on abdominal palpation.

From April to June, 1947, she remained confined to bed and her condition worsened. On account of the violent paroxysms of pain she had to have heavy doses of morphine (8 centigrammes per day). She also suffered from abundant and fetid vaginal discharge. On June 30th, 1947, she was transported to Lourdes by stretcher in an alarming and very wasted condition.

She received no treatment at Lourdes, but on the evening of July 3rd, following her third immersion in the pool, she was able to get up on her own and go to the toilet. For the first time she was able to pass stools without an enema. They were normal, and there was no evacuation of pus or of any collection of abnormal material.

Two days after her return to Nice, Dr Fay examined her and found that the rectal swelling had completely gone. She no longer suffered any pain or disturbance, but she still craved for her morphine injections, and she had to continue taking them until January, 1948. In March, 1948, an X-ray taken after a barium enema revealed no abnormality of the rectum.

On July 6th, 1948, Drs Fr. Leuret and R. Strobino carried out a rectoscopy and considered the rectum of normal appearance. Following her cure at Lourdes, Mme Martin was able to have a normal daily bowel evacuation, her vaginal discharge cleared up, she recovered her appetite and rapidly gained in weight—17 kg. in 10 months—and resumed a very active life.

On July 6th, 1948, Mme Martin was interviewed and examined at the Lourdes Medical Bureau. Her medical history was recorded in summary on the Lourdes form together with the signed comments of Dr Leuret and the other medical men present. They state that: 'In the course of a few minutes the patient recovered all her normal functions—and she has regained complete health.' Their summary report reads as follows:

Mme Rose Martin is at present completely cured. Her abdominal condition is much improved although there is still a gap of three fingers between the rectus muscles (i.e. the abdominal wall is still defective—D.J.W.), but as she has gained nearly twenty-five kilos in weight in one year this aspect of her cure can be discounted.

It is otherwise as far as the rectal tumour is concerned which has been rightly diagnosed as a pelvic recurrence of the cancer of the cervix for which she had an operation in 1946. This rectal tumour does not seem to have been thought doubtful by the surgeon who sent us his report. It seemed to him that the diagnosis was so little in doubt—bed-ridden patient, cachexia, gross tumour perceptible in all examination routes—that he abstained from ordering a biopsy, not foreseeing that it would be useful in confirming the diagnosis of secondary neoplasm. But it seems that no other diagnosis is defendable. There was no abnormal evacuation.

(Signed) Leuret, Strobino, etc. . . .

Mme Martin has remained well. Dr Ruth Cranston who visited her in 1952 writes: 'I found her in her kitchen, cooking vegetables for the mid-day soup: a sturdy nice-looking woman of fifty, very energetic' (8).

Mme Martin told Dr Cranston how she had suffered the pains of hell and had had more than 5,000 morphine injections. The Sisters of the Misericordia who looked after her in her distress prevailed upon her to go to Lourdes. Her doctor did not want her to go but she had a presentiment she could be cured and so she insisted.

So much for the medical facts as they are recorded. To sum up, Mme Martin had a very common form of cancerous growth which was removed by a standard operation. Unfortunately complications arose, the operation wound broke open, the intestines protruded and infection set in. She recovered for the moment, however, and then six months later returned complaining of pains which were apparently caused by a swelling in the bowel that could be felt by the finger. Without further investigation the doctors assumed that she had a recurrence of her cancer, and as far as one can make out the unfortunate Mme Martin was simply given up for lost.

Considering the complications the patient had undergone after her operation, and the likelihood of continued infection in her lower abdomen, it seems surprising that Dr Fay did not consider it worth while to make sure the swelling was cancerous by ordering a biopsy or at least by carrying out a rectoscopy (i.e. the insertion of an instrument enabling the inside of the bowel to be examined by direct inspection). Dr Strobino argues that the diagnosis of cancer was virtually certain and a biopsy unnecessary since the patient was bed-ridden and wasting away. As other complications besides cancer could have produced both the swelling and the wasting illness, his argument carries little conviction.

To give an example, after removal of the uterus fibrous tissue is apt to form at the site of the operation, in particular in the recto-uterine pouch, an area just in front of the rectum, and such a fibrous mass might well produce a swelling that would be felt by the examining finger as a lump in the bowel. Then again, any chronic infective process that may have been going on would not only favour fibrous reactions but might also result in swelling due to the formation of an abscess. The observation about the fetid discharges from the vagina suggests that some infection was still present. Unfortunately the dossier does not include temperature records, which would have been helpful in assessing this possibility.

The patient's general condition being very bad does favour the diagnosis of secondary cancer. Moreover, the characteristic quality of secondary cancerous tumour, which is hard and nodular, should have been recognizable to the experienced surgeon who examined her. Unfortunately he gives no description, and what is more he places the tumour at the recto-sigmoid junction, a situation normally out of reach of the examining finger. One wonders if he really did get a clear impression of the tumour via the finger in the rectum, or if he simply felt something between his finger and the hand pressing on the surface of the abdomen.

Another explanation of the lump is that it was simply a mass of impacted faeces such as occurs in severe constipation. Mme Martin was taking large doses of morphine, a drug which is renowned for causing severe constipation. The sudden resumption of bowel functions and the disappearance of the lump might have been the result of the interruption of her customary morphine injections.

That the Lourdes doctors had thought of other explanations than recurrence of cancer is indicated by their insistence that there was no abnormal evacuation of the bowels prior to the dramatic recovery. If there had been, it could have been an important point in favour of the impacted faeces or inflammatory mass interpretations, hence the importance of denying it. Unfortunately for the protagonists of the miracle cure, the Lourdes dossier contains an account by Mme Martin herself of how she passed a large amount of stinking faeces during the journey. In a letter dated May 13th, 1949, she describes how she called for the bed-pan and how the nurse remarked, '*c'est infect.*'

The nurse in question, Mlle Clory, writing on May 14th, 1949, confirms that Mme Martin used the bed-pan, but cannot recall the quality of the stools. However, she does recall that Mme Martin was constantly demanding morphine, saying that her doctor had told her she should have it whenever she needed it to ease her pain. 'Being afraid that she exaggerated,' writes Mlle Clory, 'at Lourdes I spoke to the pilgrimage doctor to ask his advice. He told me to give her instead an injection of Lourdes water and camphor. That is what I did. The patient calmed down. She no longer asked for morphine. That made me think, and I even said to my companion: "See what the imagination does." What struck me more was that the patient demanded morphine no more, neither during the last days at Lourdes nor on her return. I no longer had to concern myself with her.'

The nurse's testimony about withholding morphine may well explain the sudden relief of the patient's constipation, the passing away of the offending material, and the consequent recovery. The assertion on the Lourdes report form that the recovery took place in the space of a few minutes is a gross exaggeration. It is recorded elsewhere by Dr Strobino that the patient felt an improvement after her first immersion, but it was not until the evening of July 3rd, 1947, following her third immersion, that she became well enough to get up herself and go to the toilet. Nurse Clory's story about the effect of the substitute injection indicates that Mme Martin was susceptible to suggestive influences, even though Dr Leuret states: 'One must record that the patient shows a normal psyche, very calm. She doesn't believe in the miracle, and constantly wonders if she is really cured.'

The report of the Diocesan Canonical Commission which resulted in Mme Martin's cure being pronounced miraculous ends on this cautious note:

Some systematic minds would be able to suppose that the second phase of the illness, the post-operative phase, is susceptible to explanation in terms of an infective process following the cancer, but not intrinsically cancerous.

A supplementary inquiry having been made through the Nice medical authorities and it being impossible to remove the doubt absolutely, the Canonical Commission, to be scrupulously exact, decides to present the cure of Rose Martin as a miraculous cure of a person who had certainly been cancerous and who had as a result of the disease arrived at the very gates of death.

The present writer shares the doubts as to the condition being 'intrinsically cancerous', and therefore fails to see why her recovery was considered 'miraculous' or even particularly remarkable.

4. FRANCIS PASCAL

The child Francis Pascal, born October 2nd, 1934, was cured of partial paralysis and complete blindness at Lourdes on August 26th, 1938. On May 31st, 1949, the Archbishop of Aix, Arles and Embrun pronounced his cure miraculous. In point of fact, the diagnosis was so uncertain, and the medical information so scanty, that any interpretation is the merest guesswork.

Francis was smitten with high fever in December, 1937, his body went stiff and he was subject to constant vomiting. He was believed to be suffering from meningitis. The only available medical particulars are given in the following certificates contained in the Lourdes dossier:

I. Certificate from Dr P. Dardé on Lourdes Pilgrimage Form, August, 1938.

I, the undersigned Dr Dardé, declare I have had under my care the young Francis Pascal, 4 years old, for residual symptoms of meningitis with paralysis of the lower limbs and absolute blindness.

The above lesions, observed for the past four months, are in a static condition and do not appear to be influenced by any treatment.

II. 2nd Certificate from Dr Dardé given two months after patient's return from Lourdes.

November 9th, 1938

I, the undersigned Dr Dardé declare that I had under my care from

December 17th, 1937 to June 14th, 1938, the young Francis Pascal aged 4 years. This child, who was seen in consultation with Drs Julian of Tarascon, Barre of Avignon, Dufoix junior of Nimes, Polge, ophthalmologist, at Arles, suffered from aseptic lymphocytic meningitis (analysis from Dr Lesbros at Avignon). On the cessation of regular supervision (June 14th, 1938) this patient had paralysis of four limbs, the visual acuity was null, the child did not even perceive the light and likewise did not distinguish day from night. An examination by Dr Polge in May, 1938, led to a completely unfavourable prognosis.

Towards August 20th the child was to be taken to Lourdes with the pilgrimage from Aix and I was called in to re-examine him. The condition observed in June was unchanged, paralysis of the limbs, vision nil. On returning from Lourdes, Mme Pascal brought back the child led by the hand and walking. His walk was normal, save for a slight staggering (titubation). Since that day the improvement has been maintained and even increased.

This change came about after immersion in the pool at Lourdes. Medically, one cannot explain such a result.

(Signed) P. Dardé.

III. Certificate from Dr J. Julian.   *Tarascon sur Rhône,*
December 9th, 1938.

I, the undersigned Jean Julian, doctor of medicine, certify that I attended in March, 1938, the child, Francis Pascal, then aged 4, at his domicile at rue Camille Desmoulins, Beaucaire. This child was suffering from aseptic lymphocytic meningitis. His condition was very grave. Later on he became still worse. The four limbs were paralysed. The visual acuity became nil. The situation appeared desperate. Following a pilgrimage to Lourdes, with immersion in the pool, a notable improvement occurred, and the child whom I saw again yesterday shows only a few unimportant sequelae susceptible to further improvement.

(Signed) J. Julian.

IV. Laboratory for Medical Analyses. Duplicate of analysis of March 15th, 1938.

(Mme M. Lesbros), May 23rd, 1939.

Mr Francis Pascal, rue Camille Desmoulins, Beaucaire.

Duplicate of analysis of March 15th, 1938.

Examination of cerebro-spinal fluid

Appearance of liquid .	slightly cloudy
Cytology . .	125 leucocytes/cu. mm. in the Nageotte cell
	lymphocytes 50%
	polynuclear neutrophyle 50%
Albumen . .	0.62 G. per litre
Glucose . .	0.33 G. per litre

B.W. Reaction   .   (i.e. Bordet-Wasserman)
                            Technique of Calmette and Massol negative

Bacteriological examination.   Search for Koch's bacillus by direct
examination—negative.   Absence of bacteria.   Plating on ascitic
fluid—no microbe growth after six days of incubation.

V. Certificate from Dr E. Polge.   *Arles, December 6th*, 1938.
    I, the undersigned doctor of medicine, certify I examined young
Francis Pascal in May, 1938.   This infant was brought to me following
a meningitis (because he was paralysed and could not see).
    Ophthalmological examination May 3rd.
        The pupils react very little to light.
        Normal transparency.
        In the optic fundus veins congested and a certain degree of
    pallor of the disc.
                                            (Signed) E. Polge.

From these certificates it is far from clear what was wrong
with the child.   Details of the development of the illness and of
the physical examinations by the doctors are almost entirely
lacking.   Medical men to whom I have shown these certificates
have guessed at diagnoses as widely different as encephalitis,
poliomyelitis, Landry's paralysis, acute polyneuritis and benign lymphocytic meningitis.   All these conditions can clear
up spontaneously without complications.   Of those mentioned
the last-named, benign lymphocytic meningitis, is the most
likely diagnosis, and the one favoured by the Lourdes doctors
themselves.   But it is not a condition that usually causes blindness; normally one expects it to clear up completely in a matter
of weeks leaving behind no permanent disability.   It must be
admitted that the results of the cerebro-spinal fluid examination are not properly typical even of benign lymphocytic meningitis.   The polymorphs are too numerous and the protein too
high.

    It is conceivable that the blindness and flaccid paralysis from
which the child was suffering when he went to Lourdes was in
fact the functional aftermath of a temporary organic disturbance
which had already recovered.   It was six months after the cerebro-
spinal fluid examination that the functional recovery took place
—ample time for the organic disease to have cleared up.
Neither the blindness nor the paralysis was fully investigated,

so no one can know whether they were partly functional at the time of the visit to Lourdes. Dr Polge, the ophthalmologist, discovered no obvious reason for the apparent absolute blindness, but then in the early stages of blindness due to optic neuritis there may be no detectable changes in the optic disc. The description of the discs suggests the possibility of a mild degree of papilloedema, a recognized complication of benign lymphocytic meningitis, but this would be insufficient to account for absolute blindness. It is notoriously difficult, however, to investigate defective vision in young children owing to lack of co-operation. But the same excuse cannot be used in connection with the paralyses. Tests of reflexes, results of electrical stimulation, or examinations of separate muscle groups, all of which would have helped to establish the nature of the paralysis, are simply not given. In the absence of any conclusive evidence to the contrary, the hypothesis of a predominantly functional cure seems at least possible.

Similar considerations seem to have occurred to some of the doctors concerned in publishing the Lourdes miracles. When considering this case the Canonical Commission sought the advice of Dr Latil, a children's specialist, and Dr Charpin. They reported as follows:

Critical Comments by Drs Charpin and Latil

June 8th,
Aix-en-Provence.

Dr Pierre Latil

Consultant in Pediatrics at the Hospital

I, the undersigned, Dr Pierre Latil, declare that I have taken note of the dossier communicated to me concerning the illness affecting young Francis Pascal from December, 1937 to August, 1938. . . .

After studying this dossier we can only adopt great reserve in our conclusions, on account of the insufficiency and absence of information about the essential signs, the course of the illness, the treatment applied and the complementary examinations to which it gave rise. In particular:

1° *The signs of the illness.* The results of the neurological examination are not recorded, nor the absence or presence of certain signs having special significance. Reflexes (cutaneous and tendinous)? Loss of deep and superficial sensation? Dyspha-

gia? Involvement of sphincters? Trophic signs (amyotrophia)?
The infant's mental condition?

2° *The complementary examinations*
—No study of the electrical reactions of muscles and nerves.
—Examination of the optic fundus not repeated at the cure.
—Lumbar puncture only carried out three months after the onset
of the meningitic syndrome.

3° *Course of the illness*
How was he exactly from December, 1937 to March 1938?
Was he still febrile? At what time did the paraplegic syndrome
appear, and did it come on quickly or slowly?

4° *Treatment*
It is not said what was given.

Without wishing to deny or to contradict the facts observed by our
eminent colleagues, it seems to us impossible for the reasons given
above to come to an objective conclusion as to the organic nature of the
paraplegic syndrome or to affirm that no medical explication could be
given for the disappearance of this syndrome.

Aix. June 8th, 1947.
(Signed) Latil.

Dr E. Charpin,
    Aix-en-Provence
I, the undersigned, Dr E. Charpin, after having studied attentively
the dossier of Francis Pascal, declare myself unable to subscribe to
Dr Vallet's conclusions.

1. The organic nature of the paralyses is open to dispute,
because none of the certificates mention:
    The condition of the reflexes;
    The disturbances of sensation;
    Absence or presence or degree of muscular atrophy;
    Modifications in the electrical reactions.

2. The ophthalmologist shows himself very reserved in his
examination and his conclusions. He does not speak of the
pupillary stasis of which Dr Vallet made a point.

3. We have no precise information about the course of the illness or the treatment followed.

4. The cure was not instantaneous but only rapid, and then
again we possess no precise information as to the order of re-
appearance of movements, or of the condition of the reflexes, or
of sensation or of the muscles and nerves at the time of the cure.

In the face of this vagueness and these lacunae, the list of which
could be made longer, while heartily sharing the pleasure of the little
patient and his parents, I believe that extreme reserve is necessary in
this case.

June 10th, 1947. E. Charpin.

In spite of these comments, which seem to an independent reader very moderately expressed, and eminently reasonably argued, the Lourdes Medical Bureau held a meeting on September 1st, 1948, and, instead of ordering a further investigation, the twenty doctors present simply reaffirmed the conclusion they had previously reached that 'the cure of Francis Pascal, humanly inexplicable and in effect for ten years, is beyond the realm of natural law'. Their only comments on Dr Charpin's criticisms were that the use of the term flaccid paralysis implies that the reflexes were tested and found to be abolished—an assumption that hardly seems warranted in view of the flimsy nature of the medical certificates—and that the fact that the cerebro-spinal fluid examination was done months before the cure does not detract from the evidence but rather serves to confirm the length and gravity of the illness. (The speciousness of this argument becomes obvious if one stops to imagine what they might have said if they had had the good fortune to have available examination results immediately before and immediately after the cure.) The Canonical Commission finally approved the miracle and referred to 'the exceptional number of proofs attesting the existence of the illness and its absolute cure . . .'

One possible interpretation I have not so far mentioned. This case could have been one of those rare instances of a child surviving an attack of tuberculous meningitis without the aid of modern chemotherapeutic agents. The cerebro-spinal fluid examination was taken as excluding this possibility, but this is placing much too much reliance on a single result. It is quite usual for no bacilli to be seen microscopically even after repeated searching. The pathological report states, however, that even on culture no bacilli could be produced, but if the report is to be taken at its face value they only incubated the culture for 'six days' and one would not expect a growth in that short time. It might be that 'six days' was simply a clerical error for 'six weeks', which would be a reasonable time, but one cannot know. The severity and the long duration of the illness favour the diagnosis of tuberculosis, and so do the visual and paralytic complications, which are not features of benign lymphocytic meningitits. If this is the correct diagnosis—and we cannot be more than speculative about it—the recovery of vision would certainly be regarded as most curious. However, Dr Wickes, a London specialist in children's diseases, informs me that he has personally observed closely among his own patients a case of blindness from tuberculous meningitis that recovered contrary to all expectation, although the optic discs retained an abnormally pale, degenerative appearance. If in fact Francis Pascal had had an attack of tuberculous meningitis then these two cases show a certain parallel. Dr Wickes' case had had streptomycin, but the fact that he made a recovery indicates that, potentially at least, recovery of vision in such circumstances is not 'beyond natural law'.

The Canonical Commission's report refers to an 'absolute cure', but this is inaccurate. In 1948 Francis Pascal was examined by an ophthalmologist, Dr Lucien Bayle of Cerles, who found that the child retained a considerable defect of vision (visual acuity 1/10 and 2/10 of normal for right and left eye respectively) and that the optic disc showed the abnormal pallor associated with a nerve destroyed—or in this case partially destroyed—by inflammatory disease. His report reads as follows:

Cerles, February 26th, 1948

I, the undersigned, Dr Bayle certify that on February 14th I examined in my consulting room young Francis Pascal aged 13½, who was accompanied by his parents. The young boy's story was told me. It seems that at the age of 3 he had an attack of meningo-ophthalmic neuraxitis and was looked after at the time (1938) by Drs Dufois of Nimes, Dardé of Beaucaire, Julian of Tarascon and Dr Polge, ophthalmologist, of Arles, who observed a bilateral pupillary stasis with visual blindness, such as is encountered in 25% of these cases. Apparently the child recovered his sight and also the use of his paralysed limbs after a pilgrimage to Lourdes.

On the above date I saw Francis Pascal for the first time. He seemed a vigorous, healthy child who showed no physical or intellectual stigma. I was called upon to examine him solely from the ocular standpoint. I observed:

1. Right eye: Annexes normal, media normal, reflexes normal in both modes. Examination of the fundus showed a white optic atrophy of post-neuritic type. Vessels normal. Visual field subnormal for white, contracted for colours. Ocular tonus

normal. Vision on the Monoyer Scale at five metres shows an acuity of 1/10, not improved by lenses.

2. Left eye: Same ophthalmoscopic and general elements as on the right. Same atrophic appearance of the disc. The acuity of this eye is 2/10.

3. For near vision, reading is possible and easy at 0.3. Lenses do not seem to produce any appreciable improvement.

In summary, it is a matter of post-neuritic optic atrophy with regeneration of vision of 1/10 and 2/10, permitting normal sight, and apparently in *statu quo* since the recovery ten years ago, the character and rapidity of which were remarkable.

(Signed) Bayle.

The essential point about this partial recovery is that it took place suddenly and at Lourdes. The child was taken to Lourdes by his mother on August 23rd, 1938. On August 26th, when he was being carried back to the hospital by his mother after being immersed for the second time, he is reported to have pointed with a finger and to have remarked on the passers by. Dr Dardé saw the child on his return from Lourdes (he unfortunately gives no date, but it could have been August 28th, the day Mme Pascal returned) and notes that Francis was walking, but he gives no information about the state of the child's vision or the strength or spasticity of the affected limbs. Now it is perfectly true that the condition might have shown a swift improvement on August 23rd, but there is no medical evidence on the point. There are no records of examinations either before or after, only the mother's testimony that the child's reactions changed suddenly for the better. Even if there had been a sudden objective change, amounting to a 'miracle', the medical documentation is so poor we could never be sure about it.

In the version of this case published by Leuret (22), the medical reports and discussions are for the most part given in full, but no mention whatever is made of Drs Charpin and Latil or of their criticisms. The photostat copy of the dossier that was given to me in the first instance by the Lourdes Bureau did not include their reports, and it was not until I visited Lourdes and was able to consult the original dossier that I could read their comments.

The incompleteness of the medical evidence in this case is

particularly unfortunate because this cure is in many ways the most interesting of the official miracles. Whereas the majority of cases concern chronically ailing women whose symptoms might in part at least be psychogenic, in this case the patient was of an age when psychological invalidism is less likely. Certain points, e.g. the pallor of the optic discs and the reduced vision, establish the presence of some objective disability and give credence to the assumption that the rest of the symptoms also had an objective basis. But in the absence of a proper investigation and an established diagnosis we can only speak of what might have been.

5. COLONEL PELLEGRIN

Colonel Pellegrin visited Lourdes in October, 1950 with a discharging wound left over from an abscess of the liver which had been opened and drained by a surgeon eighteen months previously. There was some question whether the abscess was originally due to a cyst caused by an old infection with the amoeba parasite, or whether it was a tuberculous infection. Whatever its true origin, the Colonel had a discharging fistula which up to the time of his visit to Lourdes had not properly healed. His doctor, a T.B. specialist, gives the following certificate:

Dr E. Pierre,
    23 Rue Mirabeau,
        Toulon.

Medical Certificate

I, the undersigned doctor of medicine, certify as follows:

At the beginning of 1949, Colonel Pellegrin had himself admitted to the Maritime Hospital at Toulon for a painful area on his side, at the back of his chest in the region of the right base, with fever and poor general condition. On account of his colonial antecedents, and especially of an amoebic dysentery in 1928 or 1929, he was first submitted to treatment with emetine, without result. He was then given treatment with penicillin, without result. The X-ray (which I have seen) showed nothing in the lung and very little in the pleura, a very slight mistiness in the region of the base, but really very little indeed.

Examinations of sputum were negative. Stethoscopic signs null. But at the end of March a final examination having shown a single Koch's bacillus on a slide, the patient was classed as a tuberculous pleurisy and it was decided to evacuate him to the T.B. hospital. He asked for his discharge. Since the hospital laboratory re-used the glass slides, the single bacillus that was found could perhaps have come from a previous examination, having resisted the washing of the slide, an event that is well known in laboratories. Such at least was the opinion of the family doctor, one time bacteriologist in the Institut Pasteur, an opinion which I shared after seeing the patient in consultation.

The patient returned home in the same condition as when he left, suffering worse and worse in his right side. He asked his doctor to call me in, and the consultation took place at the end of March, 1949. A bulging in the next-to-last intercostal space with redness and exquisite tenderness, without any pleural or pulmonary signs, led us to the diagnosis of liver abscess, confirmed at once by puncture, which yielded a brownish pus, not very thick. The patient was transported next day to a clinic and operated on: a rather large and purulent collection was released from the liver, but the pus was a little different from the classical chocolate variety. Instant improvement, fall of temperature and disappearance of pain. We carried out several more sputum examinations for T.B. which remained all negative (the patient, being a grandfather, was concerned about being a danger to his grandchildren).

There remained naturally a drainage opening, though which discharged at first some pus, then some odd-looking serum. The opening showed no tendency to close and became fistulous. Two and a half months after the operation (June 1949) the discharge became once again frankly purulent (but this time no longer brownish but greenish) and the fever flared up again. The discharge became very abundant. I advised the patient to go to hospital for an X-ray to be taken after injection of lipiodol into the fistula.

The X-ray showed a long fistulous track leading to a 'paravertebral' cavity, but without communication with the bone. The hospital diagnosis was T.B. abscess, which led to treatment by 66 grammes of streptomycin without result, except for a lowering of the temperature which, however, remained abnormal. Intra-fistulous injections of P.A.S. were then given, also without result. The patient left hospital in November, with the local condition unimproved, and for months he went three times a week for dressings to the hospital: the purulent discharge was still very abundant and resisted all the treatments (he was even given quinine injections into the fistula).

In July, 1950, he came back to see me in the same condition. I advised him to try P.A.S. taken by mouth. He took it for twenty days. Six to eight weeks after the last dose no change could be observed.

It was in October that the patient left for Lourdes with his fistula still very active.

He came back to see me in November, cured.
A year later, October, 1951, the cure is maintained.

> (Signed) E. Pierre,
> Member of the Soc. de St Luc.

There is also a very interesting certificate from Dr Badelon, the surgeon who incised the abscess. He examined the patient in February, 1950, eight months before the Lourdes visit:

Letter from Dr Badelon

Dr Paul Badelon,
    Surgeon Urologist.   *Toulon,*
       10 Avenue Vauban,   *February 22nd,* 1950.
       Toulon.

To: Dr Laurent.
My dear Friend,
I have just seen again M. Pellegrin, for whom I incised a costal abscess about a year ago.

He is since then in superb general condition, has gained 14 kilos, but still has a small fistula at the site of the incision.

Lipiodol injection and an exploration by hollow sound shows an oblique track running posteriorly. There is almost at one point an attachment to the skin of the back.

I have come to wonder if this abscess could be of vertebral or para-vertebral origin because, on the film which has been shown me, there is a rather atypical appearance about the ninth or tenth (dorsal vertebra).

In spite of the finding, twice repeated, of staphylococci in the pus I believe it is a matter of a cold abscess and I am entirely in agreement with you on the advisability of abstaining from operating for the moment.

Perhaps a good picture of D_9 or D_{10} would be able to show in a more convincing fashion the osseous origin.

> Very cordially yours,
> (Signed) P. Badelon.

The surgeon's opinion that it was a cold abscess originating from a tuberculous infection of the spine was never confirmed. His statement about the patient's superb general condition and gain in weight is very important, since this improvement preceded the Colonel's visit to Lourdes and is not mentioned in the Canonical Commission's report.

The Canonical Commission's description of the actual cure reads as follows:

Section 2. The Fact of the Cure

The patient came to Lourdes on the Pilgrimage of The Rosary in October, 1950. Colonel Pellegrin himself declared to the Canonical Commission of Inquiry, 'I went to Lourdes not as one goes to a clinic but as one goes on a pilgrimage.' On October 1st the patient took his first bath in the pool. He felt nothing then except an impression of disagreeable cold sufficiently sharp to make him give up his second bath on the next day. He contented himself with following the exercises of the Pilgrimage during the day of October 2nd. On October 3rd, at the instigation of his wife, he bathed once more in the pool. The bearer who accompanied him hurriedly replaced his dressing impregnated with water from the pool. The patient returned to the hotel. His wife immediately re-made a dressing and noted that the orifice of the fistula was no longer running. The next morning, astonishing to note, there was no more pus on the dressing, but as it had happened that the fistula had from time to time obstructed itself spontaneously over a short period of time neither the patient nor his wife thought that there had been a cure. The patient returned to Toulon and following his return presented himself at the Maritime Hospital of Toulon to continue the series of injections of quinine into the fistula. But the nurses noted that there was no longer a fistulous orifice; in its place appeared a red patch perfectly healed over without any break in continuity. It is to be noted that since the second bath at Lourdes the patient's wife in the course of the dressing had observed neither scabs nor concretions of any sort. Only then did the patient understand that he was cured. Shortly after he presented himself to Dr Pierre to whom he was attached not only in a medical capacity but also as an old friend. Without revealing anything he said that he had come for an examination. He undressed, Dr Pierre noted with surprise the absence of a dressing and with a very great surprise the disappearance of the fistula replaced by a scar completely healed, rosy, supple, painless and non-adherent (this last characteristic being particularly unusual).

In answer to the spontaneous question of the doctor, 'But what have you done?' the ex-patient replied, with a smile of simplicity, 'I come from Lourdes' and then he told what had happened.

Dr Ruth Cranston, who interviewed the Colonel, reports him as saying: 'I was always a believer. All my family were believers—practising Christians. But it was my own idea, going to Lourdes' (8).

The essence of this case is not the actual healing (since there was no particular reason why the fistula should not have healed over sooner or later) but the coincidence between the closure of the fistula and the visit to Lourdes and the remarkable rapidity with which the healing was said to have taken place.

The Canonical Commission stress that:

1. There was in fact a serious illness in this case, because, passing into a state of chronicity, it was of a nature to lead to cachexia and ultimately to death.
The classical medications in 1950 were avowedly useless. The illness could be considered impossible, or, at least, very difficult to cure.
2. The illness was not in its decline, since the purulent discharge was still abundant. There was nothing to allow one to foresee the drying up.
3. All medications had proved useless (cf. *supra*).
4. The instantaneousness is apparent from the medical report by Dr Leuret, at the examination of October 8th, 1952. 'The scar formed instantly, or at least very rapidly.'
5. The cure was immediately complete, perfect.
6. Although there had been, before the cure, an interruption of the discharge, this was due to an accidental obstruction, which brought on, instead of an improvement, an aggravation of the condition, including pains from retention and elevation of temperature.
Thus, we must observe that the conclusions of the Canonical Inquiry lead to a demonstration that the requirements of the Church in the case of a miraculous cure have been realized.

If we are to accept the version of the dates given in the Lourdes dossier, a month elapsed between the bath at Lourdes, after which the fistula ceased to ooze, and the unspecified day 'in November' when Dr Pierre confirmed that the fistula was closed and healed over. This sequence does not seem specially remarkable. The impreciseness regarding crucial dates is typical of the general lack of precision in the Lourdes dossiers.

In this case I was fortunate in obtaining additional testimony through the good offices of Colonel C. H. Green, a Roman Catholic author of a book on Lourdes, who kindly entered into correspondence with Dr Pierre at my instigation. In a letter to Colonel Green dated July 19th, 1955, Dr Pierre wrote as follows:

Dr X supposes that there was a long interval of time between the moment when the Colonel's wife noted the drying of the fistula and the moment when the anatomical closure was officially observed. Now here is an absolutely exact chronology of the events: October 3rd, first bath in the pool at Lourdes, without apparent result. October 4th, the dressings are as soiled as they were before arrival at Lourdes.

October 5th, second bath, after which the patient returns at once to his hotel; there his wife removes the dressing impregnated with water from the pool, which had been given to him on getting out of the bath, and notes that the fistula is no longer discharging (although normally, as on the previous day, the oozing manifests constantly).

The next day, October 6th, astonishing to note, the dressing applied the previous evening is not soiled. Return to Toulon.

Back at Toulon on October 8th. The patient goes to the Maritime Hospital on October 10th for treatment (continuance of injections into the fistula, a method which up till then had given no result). This was five days after the second bath, five days almost to the hour. But the nurse no longer found the fistula, there remained only a red patch, perfectly epithelialized. The nurse advised the doctor, who in his turn then noted the closure of the fistula, its epithelialization, and the non-adherent, supple, painless nature of the red scar. It was then that the patient understood he was cured. He soon came to see me (and not in November) and showed me this scar. Thus, the medical observations were made five days after the immersion in the Lourdes pool. The very abundant discharge of pus was completely dried up ever since the patient's return to his hotel.

I have practised my profession for forty-five years, more than a half of this time in hospitals, and I have never seen a fistula, even one less than this, close up so quickly and heal over in this fashion. I must add that to this day the cure is maintained without the slightest sign of recurrence.

I must make clear also that certain publications have indicated erroneous dates in connection with the Colonel's case, for instance *La Semaine Réligieuse*. The dates which I give above are the true ones. . . .

Finally, I consider that the Colonel's own testimony and that of the nurses and of his wife would add nothing to the facts which I have just detailed. The dates given by me are indisputable; inquiry at the Maritime Hospital at Toulon would only confirm the exactness of the date, October 10th. Since five years ago the nurses have changed, some have gone on to naval ships, others have left the service. As for the Colonel, he does not much like people concerning themselves with him.

I hope that this reply will give you the means to answer the detractors' objections. I have written this very willingly, and hope you will accept my sincere compliments.

Toulon, July 19th, 1955.

(Signed) Dr E. Pierre.

The origin of the 'false dates' appears to be Dr Pierre's own signed statement in the Lourdes dossier which reads:

en octobre, le malade est parti pour Lourdes . . .
Il est revenu me voir en novembre, guéri.

When the discrepancies between his version of the dates of
cure and confirmation of cure and that version which appears
in the Lourdes dossier were pointed out, Dr Pierre wrote in
English as follows:

I am surprised at so many mistakes. That of my own statement to
Dr Leuret (November instead of October) is a mistake of copy or an
inattention. The dates of the bath are wrong even on the statement of
the Canonical Commission (3rd instead 5th October because the
statement of Lourdes Office says 3rd etc. . . .) I accord entirely with
you; such mistakes are most regrettable for Truth and Religion. Indeed the Canonical Commission is very diffident, minutely so, but
cannot always correct the papers of the cases, I suppose.

Without confirmation, it is impossible to accept Dr Pierre's
later version as necessarily the correct one. It is noteworthy
that it was the earlier and less remarkable sequence of dates
that served to convince the Lourdes Bureau, the Lourdes
National Committee, and finally the Canonical Commission.
Dr Pierre's additional evidence serves to illustrate how the
Lourdes Bureau might be able to improve their cases if they
followed them up more closely at the time.

Even accepting Dr Pierre's revised dates, coincidence is not
entirely ruled out. Given the thousands of sick who visit
Lourdes every year, like Colonel Pellegrin, many will have
conditions which might clear up spontaneously, and some of
these recoveries must by sheer chance take place during the
pilgrimages. If Colonel Pellegrin's fistula had healed a month
earlier his case would not be a matter for discussion in either
religious or medical circles.

In weighing up the coincidence hypothesis, due attention
should be given to the fact that as a result of treatment the
Colonel's fever was cured, his general health improved and his
weight increased long before he visited Lourdes. The closure
of the fistula was merely the last stage of a lengthy process of
recovery.

6. SISTER MARIE MARGUERITE

In this case there was no pilgrimage to Lourdes. The nun recovered after prayer and the taking of Lourdes water. The miracle took place on January 22nd, 1937, in the convent of Sainte Clare at Rennes, and was vouched for by the Reverend Mother Abbess and several members of the Community.

Without careful medical substantiation of such a case, the sceptically minded are unlikely to be interested. Unfortunately, the original dossier has disappeared from the Lourdes files—at any rate it was not available there when I visited the Bureau in 1955—and all that one can see is the report that was published in *Lourdes Bulletin*, No. 69, July, 1946. The case has been mentioned in a Dutch psychiatric journal by Dr S. Koster, but he gives no additional information (17). It is possible (but not, I think, very likely) that more medical data was available at the time the cure was judged miraculous, but all the doctors to whom I have shown the report agree with me that the absence of a full account of physical signs and pathological investigations makes assessment of the case impossible.

There is a short and unsatisfactory account of the illness by Dr Philouze, the nun's medical attendant. Sister Marguerite was born in 1872. Her illness began in 1924, with pains in the region of the kidney and albumen and blood in the urine. She pursued an up-and-down course for many years and each year had several attacks of haematuria. From 1926 on the condition was complicated by 'cardiac attacks of anginal type'. In 1936 Dr Blanchard, a specialist, diagnosed an abscess of the left kidney but advised against operation on account of 'the state of the heart'.

From April, 1936, onwards she suffered from generalized oedema, especially bad in the legs, where vesicles formed, which broke and led to a permanent discharge. To remain in bed became impossible, and from May onwards the patient had to remain day and night seated in an armchair; the slightest effort bringing on a cardiac attack followed by violent facial neuralgia. Up to January 22nd, 1937, this extremely distressing condition continued without improvement, and it seemed that it must soon lead to a fatal issue.

According to the nun's own testimony, she had no hope of cure and wanted the good Lord to take her as quickly as possible. She submitted as a duty to associating herself with a novena soliciting her cure because this was ordered by the Reverend Mother. She writes: 'I accepted in good heart, but begged our Reverend Mother to authorize me to stop all treatment and to take some Lourdes water so that the intervention of the Very Holy Virgin would be better appreciated.' The novena began in the evening of January 20th. In the evening of January 22nd she had an inspiration to drag herself next door to the oratory to witness Mass. Suddenly she found herself standing, and experienced a feeling of lightness and well-being. Her bandages fell to the ground and she saw that the swelling had gone and her legs were healed. From then on she walked about on her own. Next day she went out and visited Dr Philouze who wrote:

The same day or the day after her cure Sister Marguerite entered the consulting room, absolutely cured, walking normally. . . . I realized there was no longer anything the matter with her. Nevertheless I had an analysis of urine carried out; no albumen, no B. coli. I also observed that her legs were completely cured, neither oedema nor ulcers any longer present. . . .

Unfortunately, we are not told how long it was since Dr Philouze had last *examined* Sister Marguerite, although he does state that he saw her a week before her cure.

Dr Philouze gives his evidence in 1945, eight years later, when the cure was investigated by a Commission appointed by the Archbishop of Rennes. He stated: 'I did not prepare a written report [at the time], but I took full notes of all the important points, and I have kept them. They have enabled me to make a medical report on the cure seven years after.'

In 1945 Sister Marguerite was examined by three doctors who found her healthy, with heart sounds normal and well-marked, kidneys neither palpable nor tender and no oedema.

The war is given as the reason for the long delay in submitting the case to the Lourdes Bureau, but in fact the cure took place nearly three years before the outbreak of war. Brief as I have made the summary of the case, it includes all the medical data given, and any doctor would appreciate that the nature of the illness is far from clear. Although 'cardiac attacks of anginal type' and poor 'state of the heart' are mentioned, there is no note of actual signs and symptoms of heart failure, such as enlargement of liver, engorgement of jugular veins, *râles* heard at the bases of the lungs, or breathlessness. There is no mention of X-rays showing enlarged heart or diseased kidney. Some at least of the symptoms might have been due simply to a stone in the kidney, but there is no knowing if this possibility was investigated. On the whole, the description suggests some form of nephritis, although certainly an atypical variety, but the only diagnosis stated is 'abscess on the left kidney', which is quite different. There is no mention of blood pressure readings, though high blood pressure is a prominent and essential feature of many forms of kidney disease, and although Dr Philouze does mention deterioration of vision at one point there is no description of the appearance of the vessels of the retina. These two points are fundamental to the most elementary clinical examination of a patient with kidney trouble. Urine analysis is mentioned, but no details are given of dates or results. We do not know if microscopic examinations of the urine were carried out, although again these form part of the elementary clinical routine in such cases. Likewise there is no mention of the blood chemistry. In short, we are told practically nothing, and Dr Philouze reveals in his account such a surprising lack of appreciation of the sort of information required that one cannot place much confidence in his medical judgment. Simply on the information given, it could be held that the patient at the time of the 'miracle' was no longer suffering from kidney disease but simply had swelling of the legs from some local cause. This may seem implausible, but it is up to the medical men who claim a 'miracle' to prove the contrary.

7. MLLE CANIN

This woman was allegedly cured of tubercular peritonitis when she visited Lourdes in October, 1947. She was then aged 37. The abdomen was believed to have been infected from an old Pott's Disease (T.B. of the spine) for which she had been treated some years previously. The evidence that she did have cured Pott's Disease is good, but the evidence that she had active tubercular peritonitis is flimsy.

The essential points of her case history as given on the Lourdes first examination form are as follows. Born 1910, her illness began in 1934 with pains in the back, night sweats and loss of weight. After two years of this—during which time she never took her temperature—she was admitted to a Preventorium. X-rays of lung were normal and she had no skin reaction. However, in November, 1936 she had an X-ray at a Marseilles hospital, the Pott's Disease was discovered (affecting the 4th and 5th dorsal vertebrae) and she was put in a plaster cast for ten months. In September, 1937, she was transferred to the Hyères Sanatorium, where she was without a plaster but laid flat on a hard bed. This time the skin test was positive, indicating that she had been infected by tuberculosis.

At this point the abdominal symptoms began. She had digestive disturbances, vomiting, alternating diarrhoea and constipation, but no blood in the stools. She was treated with ultra-violet light (a recognized treatment for abdominal T.B.) and in 1938 her abdomen was opened and explored and her appendix removed. There is no record of what the surgeon found in the abdomen, or of any sample being taken for microscopic examination or for culture of the bacillus of tuberculosis. However, the fact that the surgeon removed the appendix suggests that he suspected chronic appendicitis rather than tuberculosis.

Following this operation she had urinary infection and also an attack of partial intestinal obstruction. Up to December, 1938 she had a fixation abscess. There was no improvement in her condition, but she was given an orthopaedic apparatus stretching from neck to sacrum which enabled her to walk. An improvement in her abdominal symptoms followed.

In November, 1939 she started to complain of pains in the right hip. She was again put in a plaster cast and laid flat until September, 1941, and during this time she again suffered alternating diarrhoea and constipation.

In September, 1941, equipped with the same orthopaedic apparatus as before, she returned to her family and was able to return to active work. She remained in work intermittently for the next three years, but in June, 1944 abdominal symptoms and pains in the hips returned.

She had some X-rays in December, 1944 and the radiologist supplies the following certificate:

I, the undersigned, certify that I examined Marie Canin on the 8th December, 1944, she was then aged 32 years and domiciled at Marseilles.

This person complained of pains in the right hip radiating into the buttock and right thigh; she suffered more and more from the right posterior portion of the pelvis and also from the right foot.

The examination showed an important limitation of movement of the right hip with pain on movement. Palpation and pressure on the right sacro-iliac joint was painful and a thickening was perceptible in the right iliac fossa without it being possible to show a fluctuation due to an abscess in that region.

The patient did not complain of pains in the dorsal spine, but examination of the X-rays confirmed the existence of an old Pott's Disease of the 9th, 10th and 11th dorsal vertebrae and showed an affection of the right sacro-iliac joint.

In summary, this person showed an old dorsal inferior Pott's Disease and a right sacro-coxyalgia for which I advised rest during eighteen months and a sacro-iliac arthrodesis. Signed G. Roudil, Marseilles, October 27th, 1947.

In January, 1945 she has an operation for fixing the spine (Albée graft), her abdominal symptoms improve and in July, 1945 she gets up. In October, 1945 she resumes work.

In June, 1946 she stops work on account of loss of weight and poor general health. In January, 1947 she has a return of her vomiting and diarrhoea. She stays at home in bed looked after by her medical man, Dr Sivan, who supplies the following medical certificate which she brings to Lourdes:

Marseilles, September 15th, 1947.

I, the undersigned, Dr Sivan, certify that Mlle Marie Thérèse Canin is suffering from dorso-lumbar Pott's Disease.

In the last three months the general condition of the patient has been very bad. She can scarcely eat anything on account of violent abdominal pains which follow the ingestion of any food, even liquid. Intestinal evacuation is very painful and is accompanied by the discharge of mucopurulent secretion.

In addition the patient complains of violent headaches with dizziness and stiffness of the neck. Frequently there appear crises of intense sweating with cardiac collapse.

In summary, this is a very serious illness with peritoneal, intestinal and vertebral tubercular lesions which have led to a very advanced state of malnutrition and toxicity.

(Signed) J. Sivan.

In a later account (October, 1948) Dr Sivan gives a few further details:

The neck region became painful and the general state worsened. In January, 1947 the patient was obliged to have another period of bed rest. From this date up to her departure for Lourdes the tubercular infection developed in the peritoneum leading to a very grave state of malnutrition.

Although not having actual paraplegia, she had not the strength to move her lower limbs which, in spite of the use of gutter splints, became affected by painful oedema.

The abdomen was distended with flatus and painful on palpation, with zones of guarding. Evacuation of the intestine was difficult and enemas were very painful and led to a state of collapse. In July a greenish vaginal discharge appeared through a vaginal fistula and became more and more profuse. There was cystitis and urinary incontinence. Further complication appeared during the summer months consisting of very violent attacks of cervical pain with dizziness and stiffness of the neck and nausea, which raised the possibility of meningitic involvement.

During the same period the patient had great difficulty in feeding and only small quantities of liquid could be absorbed. The buccal cavity was the seat of ulcerations and of thrush. The temperature oscillated about 38° to 38½° C. Attacks of cardiac collapse were frequent and the usual cardiac stimulants eventually came to have but slight effect.

It was in this state of cachexia, advanced tuberculosis, florid tubercular peritonitis and meningitic signs, with no hope of recovery, that the patient departed for Lourdes.

There is no doubt that Mlle Canin was in a very weak and debilitated condition. The religious sisters who nursed her give long confirmatory accounts of her poor condition. In June, 1947 she obtained the benefit of the law of July 14th, 1905, art. 20a, which provides assistance for the aged, the infirm and the incurable. It is less certain what she was suffering from.

Dr Sivan's account is highly inadequate. He makes no mention of vaginal or rectal examinations, which would be normal routine in such a case. He mentions vaginal fistula, but in the absence of a vaginal examination, it seems likely that she was simply suffering from a non-specific vaginal discharge such as frequently occurs in debilitated patients. Dr Sivan mentions none of the classic signs of abdominal tuberculosis, such as fluid levels in the abdomen or doughiness or palpable lumps. He describes an abdomen distended with gas, which is not typical. The symptoms as he describes them suggest some septic and possibly obstructive process in the abdomen, but he advances no clear evidence that it was tuberculous in nature. There were no proper pathological investigations, no barium enemas, no X-rays of abdomen—which might have revealed fluid levels. Worst of all, Dr Sivan shows a considerable bias towards an interpretation in terms of tuberculosis, which would make the cure more 'miraculous'.

Mlle Canin arrived at Lourdes on a stretcher on October 6th, 1947, and was housed in the Asile. In the afternoon of October 9th she felt strong enough to get up. She sat on her bed, put on some slippers (which she had not been able to do for nine months) walked without difficulty, and in the evening ate the hospital meal. Next day she was able to follow the pilgrimage exercises without help and to visit the Lourdes Medical Bureau for examination.

At the Medical Bureau Mlle Canin was noted to be 'markedly wasted, pale, voluble and emotional'. On examination the doctors noted her various operation scars, which were consistent with her medical history, but found no sign of active disease.

They reported: 'Active and passive movements of the spine sluggish. Taking into account the Albée graft, movement had normal range. Palpation and percussion revealed a zone of slight painfulness in the region of the first to third dorsal vertebrae. Active and passive movements and palpation of other articulations provoked no pain. The range of movements was normal.'

Dr Sivan followed his patient thereafter and noted a rapid increase in weight and a 'continued progressive improvement of her general condition'. On July 1st, 1948 she entered a convent. On January 30th, 1949 Dr Sivan, who was still in touch with her, wrote to confirm that her health remained normal.

The case was presented to the National Committee in Paris by the surgeon Dr Oberlin. He sums up the matter as follows:

Is the nature of the peritonitis rigorously established? We lack information about the operations in 1938, but the tuberculosis could have reached the peritoneal cavity after that date. I had asked Dr. Sivan to let me have for your inspection the X-ray photos, so as to have confirmation of the nature of the vertebral lesions, but he has replied that the X-rays, which are old, have not been carefully conserved, and were already unreadable last summer. Nevertheless, clinically, the existence of a peritonitis with a vaginal fistula is firmly established and so is the extreme gravity of the patient's general condition when she arrived at Lourdes.

Was the cure instantaneous? If this qualification cannot be applied to the case absolutely literally, nevertheless the transformation of Mlle Canin's condition was sufficiently rapid to be beyond all scientific explanation. Finally, the cure has been maintained now for sixteen months, so it seems the case of Mlle Canin should be retained by the Medical Committee.

(Signed) Oberlin, February 23rd, 1949.

Unless Dr Oberlin had available more evidence than is given in the dossier, one cannot but heartily protest against his view that the existence of a T.B. peritonitis was firmly established on clinical grounds. The fact that he is capable of putting forward a statement so evidently biased casts doubt on the other cases (e.g. Pellegrin, Martin) in which he has pronounced in favour of the miraculous. All one can say of this case is that the patient suffered from a long-standing but fluctuating abdominal disturbance of undetermined origin. It could have been in part functional. She had recovered several times before, and she recovered again very rapidly after her visit to Lourdes. Such an event deserves no special comment.

In April, 1950 the cure was pronounced miraculous. In coming to their decision, the Canonical Commission took into account the fact that 'the marvellous cure . . . took place in favour of a good Christian who, after her cure, evinced a desire to give herself further to God'.

8. LOUISE JAMAIN

On December 14th, 1951 a Diocesan Commission appointed by Monseigneur Feltin, Archbishop of Paris, pronounced in favour of the miraculous nature of Mlle Louise Jamain's recovery from pulmonary tuberculosis on the occasion of her second pilgrimage to Lourdes in April, 1937. Although the case is an old one, it was doubtless singled out for official proclamation because of the unusual detail of the clinical records. Mlle Jamain was under the care of a Paris hospital when she left for Lourdes, and she returned to the hospital for further investigation following her cure.

Born November 1st, 1914, she was healthy up to 13 years of age, although four of her five brothers died in childhood of pulmonary tuberculosis—according to the history she gave to Dr Lefranc, the Lourdes pilgrimage doctor. At 13 she underwent an operation for appendicitis, after which she had to enter the sanatorium at Hendaye for six months on account of a persistent abdominal fistula. Dr Lefranc's notes refer to this as a tuberculous infection, but no details are given and the surgeon, Dr Oberlin, who treated her subsequently, does not mention tuberculosis.

Four years later (October, 1930) Louise Jamain entered hospital again with painful attacks of colic and signs of partial intestinal obstruction. Dr. Oberlin performed several operations. He found the disturbance to be due to subacute volvulus of the sigmoid colon which was a consequence of congenital megacolon. (No mention of abdominal tuberculosis.) This was treated by establishing an artificial caecal fistula, to relieve the obstruction, and later resecting the affected loop of intestine. In November, 1931 the artificial fistula was closed and soon after the recovered patient left hospital.

According to the history she gave Dr Lefranc, after this she had a pulmonary congestion with pleural effusion and she was sent to the Villepinte sanatorium and later transferred to the Champrosay preventorium. She dates the pleural effusion as March, 1931 and the transfer to Champrosay as the end of 1931, but presumably this is a mistake for March and December, 1932. Up to this point all her sputum examinations were negative, only the stools showed the presence of tuberculous bacilli. (Dr Lefranc.)

In point of fact, chronologically, the next medical document in the Lourdes files after Dr Oberlin's certificate is a certificate from Champrosay provided so that she might join a Lourdes pilgrimage in April, 1933:

Preventorium of Champrosay

I, the undersigned, Dr Hiel, certify that Mlle Louise Jamain, six times operated on for intestinal perforation and complications, is now convalescing in Champrosay in a sub-febrile state, and that her condition allows of her making the journey from Paris to Lourdes and back with an organized pilgrimage.

It is curious that this certificate makes no mention of tuberculosis.

Mlle Jamain visited Lourdes in April and later in the year (possibly the summer, but the record is undated) called at the Medical Bureau where the following note was made:

A young woman in good health. Shows several surgical scars on her abdomen. A scar from a fistula, which she told us had closed up at the pool on April 20th last, is perfect and leaves no visible orifice. The doctor at Champrosay will have noted this closure on the young woman's return to the sanatorium.

The Lourdes file contains no record of whether the doctor at Champrosay confirmed the closure of the fistula (indeed this is the only suggestion that she had an open fistula at this period), there is merely a note on the file which reads:

Case classified. Cure by amelioration—having preceded by three weeks her coming to Lourdes.

Although no special claims are made about the result of this first visit to Lourdes, I have included an account of it because of the doubt cast on the accuracy of the history of long-standing abdominal tuberculosis, and also because it is important, in view of what comes later, to know whether this patient was a person likely to try to exaggerate the gravity of her illness.

The next medical report is from Dr Jacquelin, who, at Mlle Jamain's request, after her cure, sends her a copy of the notes he made when he examined her at his consulting room on July 20th, 1936.

Admitted to Bon Secours in 1936 with acute attacks and a temperature of 40° C. Was sent there for operation for presumed cholecystitis. Hardly had she been admitted when she developed jaundice. Examination showed only a pain in the gall bladder region, and my advice as to an operation was not acted upon. All the signs improved little by little and she increased in weight by 3 kg.

At present she comes (July 20th, 1936) to see me again on account of a recurrence of pains and of vomiting; the pains are located in the right side and scapula, they are often severe; vomiting comes on sometimes in the daytime but in the morning before eating. Temperature develops about 38° C.; the stools are discoloured. Menstruation, habitually regular, has ceased for three months; she does not cough.

Physical examination. Three scars on the abdomen; the patient attributes these to three operations, in 1932 for appendicitis, then for peritonitis. Diffuse resistance of the whole abdomen. Diffuse sensitiveness, most marked in the right sub-costal zone. Weight 52 kg. 300. Differential diagnosis between: cholecystitis or tubercular peritonitis of sub-hepatic localization.

There is also the following report of an X-ray examination dated July 27th, 1936:

1. Radiography of the gall bladder after periodic ingestion of tetra-iodo-phenophthalein. A film taken about fifteen hours after the last ingestion shows: a well impregnated bladder, situated high and external, of regular opacity, volume and contour. Pressure on the

bladder is clearly painful. A second film taken several hours after the first and after a meal shows that the bladder is very poorly evacuated; it remains clearly impregnated with tetra-iodo-phenophthalein.

2. Radiography after a barium meal. Stomach; short, high situation stretched (*en écharpe*). The pylorus is displaced to the right, pulled towards the gall bladder. There is no localized alteration in the contour or the surface of the stomach image. Hypertonia, hyperkinesis, pyloric passage rapid. Global evacuation complete after the usual time.

Duodenum. The bulb is thrown to the left by the hepato-vesicular mass, in particular the bladder produces a depression on the right side of the bulb. The second part of the duodenum receives an even, clear imprint from the gall bladder; in its upper portion it describes a veritable spiral closely embracing the left border of the vesicle. There is a certain amount of duodenal stasis.

Intestine. After the sixth hour the barium has been completely evacuated from the stomach and the ileum and occupies the large intestine up to the neighbourhood of the splenic angle. Spastic appearance.

In summary. Signs of cholecystitis and of localized sub-hepatic peritonitis.

If Mlle Jamain had had tuberculous enteritis for many years there is surprisingly little to show for it in this X-ray examination. The history, as given to Dr Lefranc, continues as follows:[1]

The same day (i.e. July 27th, 1936) a chest X-ray was taken, but the patient does not have the report.

On August 3rd, 1936 she enters the Cochin Hospital, under Dr Boulin. Several intubations are carried out. Operation on October 3rd, 1936, but details are not available. It seems that she had irradiation of the peritoneum with ultra-violet, the existence of a T.B. peritonitis having been previously postulated.

After the operation she was transferred to the medical service and treated with ultra-violet. It seems that a generalized peritonitis ensued with very considerable ascites which, on drainage, yielded 9 litres of fluid. Injections of antigen, methylene, etc.

During the three weeks following the operation there is a clear improvement and a regain of weight. She is given five blood transfusions in ten days, in all 1,100 gm. of blood.

Then she starts to vomit again, constipation so intense that the construction of another artificial anus is considered.

During November, 1936 has a pulmonary congestion. Starts to run a temperature again towards the end of December. Taking no solid food. About January 22nd, evening temperature 39°–39.5° C.

[1] This version differs slightly from that given by Dr Vallet in *La Verité sur Lourdes*, but I have tried to keep to the original notes in the Lourdes file.—D.J.W.

She is moved after this to the Laennec Hospital (under Professor Besançon); Dr Pergola is the senior hospital officer. Examination of sputum and stools both positive for T.B. Took no more solid food after January 22nd—given serum, camphorated oil, milk and champagne. She decides to visit Lourdes again against the advice of the doctors.

Sunday evening, the evening of her departure. Temperature 39.9° C. She has a haemoptysis in the train (ergot, morphine, etc.). On Monday, the day of her arrival at Lourdes, attacks of dyspnoea, suffocation, cardiac deficiency, two haemoptyses (ergotine, morphine, etc.).

Tuesday morning, two or three haemoptyses. Tuesday afternoon, after an haemoptysis, suffocation, believes that she is dying.

In the night of Wednesday to Thursday, very excited, wakes up saying she has slept very well. At mid-day eats for the first time, without vomiting at all in the afternoon. Eats in the evening, sleeps well, takes breakfast on Friday, goes to the pool. Temperature on leaving the pool 36.5° C., lunches, no vomiting.

Temperature this morning, April 3rd, 1937, 37° C.

(Signed) G. Lefranc. April 3rd, 1937.

(Doctor in charge of pilgrimage.)

The latter part of the story is confirmed by several medical certificates.

Dr Pergola, writing from the Laennec Hospital, sends his opinion to the patient's doctor in the following terms.

February 13th, 1937.

My dear Colleague,

Your patient now shows an almost complete intolerance of food, due to a tuberculous peritonitis of occlusive type of long standing.

Her pulmonary state is satisfying, but her entero-peritoneal condition seems to me to give the total situation a grave prognosis.

Sincerely,

(Signed) Pergola.

There is also a certificate from Dr Cachin, pupil of Professor Besançon, who continued to see the patient after she left hospital.

Dispensair Léon Bourgeois

I, the undersigned, Chef de Clinique to the Faculty, certify that Mlle Louise Jamain, hospitalized at Laennec from January 21st to March, 1937, showed, at that date, according to the examinations carried out by the hospital, a positive bacilloscopy contrasting with a normal radiological appearance, but coincident with an irregular, raised temperature.

In the course of a further hospitalization, on April 4th, 1937, the patient was apyretic, bacteriological examinations were negative of sputum and of stools.

Since then, further examinations of sputum and stools have remained negative. She is at present in excellent general condition and the X-ray picture (July 23rd, 1937) is normal.

This certificate has been issued at the patient's request.

(Signed) Cachin.

July 24th, 1937.

A letter from the Abbé Bouyer, Chaplain to the Laennec Hospital, confirms that at the instigation of one of the hospital doctors, who believed she was too ill to stand the journey, he tried to prevail upon Mlle Jamain to postpone her visit to Lourdes.

Photostat copies of the hospital temperature chart are available showing a striking increase of hectic fever reaching maxima of 104.4° F., 105.4° F., 105.1° F., and finally 104.0° F. on the last four days before she departed for Lourdes. The records following her return to hospital five days later show the fever completely subsided. The hospital documents also record the presence of bacilli on five occasions when the sputum was examined (fifteen per field on February 26th), and the injections of serum, camphorated oil and caffeine which were used to sustain this very sick patient.

Mlle Jamain appeared before the Medical Bureau on April 3rd, 1937. Her haemorrhages had ceased, she was eating well and having normal bowel evacuations. The Lourdes examination notes record:

Pulmonary examination. Slight dullness to percussion on the right, in the upper third. On asculation slight diminution of vesicular murmur in the same situation.

Abdomen supple, painless, no meteorism, no ascites.

Numerous operation scars.

Heart normal.

Weight 42 kg. 300.

Thereafter, Mlle Jamain rapidly gained weight and strength, her sputum remained free from bacilli, and she has since retained good health and become a happy wife and mother.

This is a complicated case. One has to distinguish between
the history elicited from the patient by the pilgrimage doctor
and the facts given in the medical certificates.

The Laennec hospital records are the most important. They
show that in March, 1937 she was spitting blood, running a
hectic fever, producing sputum laden with T.B. bacilli, and
appearing to be very ill. In striking contrast to these grave
signs, the X-rays showed no abnormality of the lungs, a most
unusual and paradoxical situation if in fact her condition was
due to advanced pulmonary tuberculosis. It is possible that the
blood and bacilli were coming from lesions in the bronchi, and
that the lungs were hardly affected, but the gravity and chronicity of the illness are scarcely consistent with this explanation.

The intubations, the laparotomy, the tapping of ascitic fluid
from the abdomen, which might provide conclusive evidence of
tuberculous peritonitis, all took place in the Cochin Hospital,
and none of their records appear in the Lourdes file. This is a
most regrettable omission. Most of the medical certificates
seem to have been produced in response to the patient's own
request. Although she succeeded in obtaining the less conclusive X-ray report prior to her admission, there is nothing to
show in the Lourdes file that either she or the Medical Bureau
tried to secure any confirmation from the Cochin Hospital.

Dr Pergola's letter from the Laennec Hospital suggests that
he accepted without question the presence of tuberculous enteritis and peritonitis, but on what evidence we do not know.
He may have been guided by the history, or there may have been
current abdominal signs and symptoms, he does not say. Dr
Lefranc's notes mention the presence of T.B. bacilli in the
stools when Mlle Jamain was in the Laennec Hospital, but there
is no mention of this in those of the Laennec records that are
available.

It has been pointed out early on that Mlle Jamain gave
Dr Lefranc the impression that she had suffered from some
form of abdominal tuberculosis since the age of 13, but that
this supposition does not seem to be confirmed by the medical
certificates produced in connection with her first Lourdes visit
in 1933. Also her claim in 1933 that a fistula had closed up

when she bathed at the pool seems to have remained uncon-
firmed. Dr Vallet, in his account of the case in *La Verité sur
Lourdes*, describes the 1933 visit, but makes no mention of the
healed fistula.

Dr Guarner includes the case of Mlle Jamain in his thesis on
Lourdes cures (13). He writes:

> But first of all, struck by the definite absence of physical and radio-
> logical signs in the lungs, and by the lack in the dossier (which could
> be improved in this regard) of any mention of objective observations
> clinical or otherwise to confirm the presence of intestinal and peri-
> toneal lesions, and struck by the contrast of this lack with the richness
> of the general and functional signs, let us examine the hypothesis of
> simulation.
> Certainly it would be possible in a T.B. ward for an impostor to
> change his sputum cup with that of a neighbour who is definitely in-
> fected and is expectorating blood and bacilli.
> Certainly a temperature could be faked. . . . Of course the other
> functional signs would then have to be imitated: dyspnoea, thoracic
> pains, vomiting . . .

After some discussion Dr Guarner dismisses this theory on
the following grounds.

1. Mlle Jamain's family background of tuberculosis.
2. Her own medical history, including tuberculous peritonitis verified by laboratory tests in August, 1936.
3. The impossibility that the Laennec Hospital authorities,
   who had themselves noted the disparity between the
   functional and the physical signs, could have overlooked
   the simple possibility of malingering.
4. The haemoptyses during the journey to Lourdes confirmed
   by Dr Lefranc.
5. The convincing character of the temperature variations
   on the Laennec Hospital chart.
6. The patient's great loss of weight.

One would agree that simple malingering seems a most
improbable explanation in the case of a woman who had a
succession of indisputably organic illnesses, but some of
Dr Guarner's arguments are open to dispute. Items 1 and 2
depend on the patient's testimony. (Incidentally, although

Dr Guarner, following Dr Vallet's published version of the case, credits Mlle Jamain's parent with having tuberculosis, this point is by no means certain from Dr Lefranc's notes.) Item 5 is doubtful in view of the fact that Mlle Jamain's occupation when fit was student nurse. Item 3 is a matter of opinion. Civilian hospitals are not geared to the investigation of malingering. The hypothesis could be rendered more plausible if one imagines that Mlle Jamain—a genuinely sick person— exaggerated her condition in various ways, both by deliberate and by unconscious hysterical reactions.

The evidence being so uncertain, the degree of importance with which these suspicions are regarded will inevitably vary according to individual predilections and bias. Perhaps the suspicions would not have arisen at all had the records been more complete and included the crucial evidence from the Cochin Hospital.

It is a sad and tantalizing reflection that in the one Lourdes miracle in which objective hospital tests are available both immediately before and immediately after the cure there should be conflict between the bacteriological and radiological findings and consequent doubt as to the interpretation of the case.

9. JEANNE FRETEL

This is perhaps the best known and one of the most interesting of the Lourdes miracle cases. The following summary appears at the beginning of the Lourdes dossier:

Mlle Jeanne Fretel, born May 7th, 1914. Came to Lourdes in October, 1948, with the Diocesan Pilgrimage of Rennes.

The first examination at the Bureau Medical was carried out October 9th, 1948. The second examination October 5th, 1949.

The diagnosis carried at the time of the first examination is: peritoneal tuberculosis with cachexia and hectic fever ranging from 40° C. to 37° C.

The patient was suddenly relieved. All symptoms disappeared, although the streptomycin used for treatment had been discontinued four months before.

The twenty-eight doctors who signed the report conclude: 'There is no medical explanation of this cure. This cure is outside natural laws.'

The patient arrived at Lourdes on October 8th, 1948, in an alarming state. Her clinical report taken at the Hôtel Dieu de Rennes under Dr Pellé said: 'From August, 1948 to October the patient becomes more and more feeble, she can only take small quantities of liquid; meningitic signs were appearing. The abdomen is very distended and very painful. Pus runs abundantly from the natural outlets—stools and vomit—accompanied by black blood. Cardiac attacks are very frequent and endanger the patient's life. All hope seems lost. It is in a florid state of tubercular peritonitis, with meningitic phenomena superadded, and in a very grave condition of cachexia that the patient —who receives three injections of morphine per day—departs for Lourdes completely prostrate'—report by Dr Pellé of Rennes.

On October 8th the patient feels better after the communion at the Autel de Bernadette. She takes some milk which she does not vomit. Taken later to the Grotto, she notes that her abdomen has returned to normal. She sits up on her stretcher at midday and takes a substantial meal. She goes on foot to the bath; has another normal meal in the evening and in the night wakes up only to complain of hunger. Having eaten, she falls asleep. She departs in good condition without any sedative.

On her return she is seen again at Rennes in the service of Dr Pellé who finds that the patient—who had received a certificate of incurability—has returned from Lourdes completely cured, having none of the symptoms that formerly she presented—normal temperature, progressive increase of weight, just above 44 kg. in October, 1948 to 58 kg. in 1949. The patient has returned to her active work; rises at five-thirty, retires at eleven-thirty in the evening. . . .

Mlle Jeanne Fretel obtained from Professor Pellé, under whose care she was at the hospital at Rennes, the following answers to the Lourdes pilgrimage questionnaire form:

Fretel, Jeanne. Hôpital Pontchaillou.

[History.] T.B. peritonitis. The patient has had seven abdominal operations since 1938. Completely bed-ridden the last three years, she takes very little nourishment and her abdominal pains keep her almost totally immobile.

[Diagnosis] T.B. peritonitis.

[Prognosis] very grave.

[Is the disease incurable?] Yes.

[Have there been surgical interventions?] September, 1942; December, 1946; January, 1938; January, 1939; May, 1941; December, 1941.

[Hospital?] Hôtel Dieu, Rennes.
[Surgeon?] Doctor Marmelle.
[Progress?] There is a progressive worsening of her state.
[Radiographs?] 5th and 6th December, 1946. No pulmonary disease.
[Analyses?] Bacteriological exam. [of sputum on] December 8th [1946] did not reveal the presence of Koch's bacillus.
[How will the patient travel?] Completely flat, stretcher case.
[Signed and dated] A. Pellé, Rennes. August 10th, 1948.
[Also signed and dated] Rennes, August 10th, 1948. J. Fretel.

The full clinical notes from the Hôtel Dieu at Rennes are available in the Lourdes file. The essential points are as follows:

Parents alive and well. Two sisters and a brother all well. A maternal uncle and a paternal aunt both died of tuberculosis. Usual childhood ailments. Her trouble began in January, 1938 when she was working as maidservant in a private house.

She experienced a sharp pain in the right iliac fossa, accompanied by vomiting and raised temperature. An urgent appendicectomy was carried out in the Hôtel Dieu at Rennes. In spite of this she continued to experience the same abdominal pains. She nevertheless resumed her work, but after two months she felt so exhausted she had to go to rest at her parents' home, where she remained until January, 1939.

During this time she suffered from anorexia, lassitude and profuse night sweats. Her abdominal pains became more severe and more persistent and constipation gave place to alternating constipation and diarrhoea.

In July, 1938, the patient, who at this time was getting up a little each day, noted that her abdomen was gradually swelling and that its consistency was becoming a little harder, more doughy. But after four months this increase in volume disappeared completely and spontaneously as a result of ultra-violet radiation.

In January, 1939, the patient, who was completely confined to bed and suffering a lot, was again hospitalized in the Hôtel Dieu, St. Philomena Ward, at Rennes. There they temporized two months and then in March intervened surgically for tuberculous ovarian cyst with adhesions. The immediate post-operative period was satisfactory, the wound closed rapidly, and no suppuration appeared.

At the beginning of August, 1939, the patient left the Hôtel Dieu.

She was no longer suffering, but the periods of constipation and diarrhoea alternated as before.

She resumed her employment from August, 1939 to March, 1940. From August to September, 1939, her condition was relatively satisfactory.

In September the patient noted that her abdomen was becoming painful, and especially so at those times of day when the more violent attacks used to appear. At the same time the abdomen became stretched, hard and increased in size.

From September, 1939 to March, 1940 all these symptoms progressively worsened, so much so that on March 18th, 1940 the patient was again hospitalized, this time in Nôtre Dame Ward. There her pains were treated with applications of ice without any surgery. At the end of June, 1940 the patient was transferred to the medical service, St. Anne Ward, where she remained until March, 1941. The condition did not improve, and in March, 1941 she was re-admitted to St. Philomena Ward. Applications of ice were continued, and in May, 1941 the surgeon, having renewed the diagnosis of tuberculous peritonitis, carried out a laparotomy. Following this intervention a fistula became established at the site of the umbilicus, a fistula communicating with the small intestine.

Faecal matter escaped through this fistula. It persisted until December, 1941, when a further operation was carried out to close it. But a few days after the operation the fistula reopened spontaneously at the same spot and faecal matter once again passed through the orifice. The fistula persisted and they temporized. In April, 1942 the patient was hospitalized in the Pontchaillou division. In September, 1942 a further operation was carried out for closure of the fistula. Two days later the fistula reappeared. In July, 1943 a further operation was unsuccessful, for five days later the fistula reappeared with exactly the same characteristics as before and even bigger. Two months later a further closure in September, 1943. Re-opened September 4th, 1944. The fistula persisted until November, 1944. In November, 1944 the patient was seen again at the Hôtel Dieu, St. Philomena Ward, and the surgeon attempted another closure of the fistula. The fistula was closed this time and has remained so up to the present.

But the abdomen has stayed bloated, hard, with a doughy consistency, and the alternating periods of diarrhoea and constipation have succeeded each other without remission in spite of the successive operations.

In January, 1945, in spite of her state, she resumed work as a maid, but could not continue more than three weeks. She rested two weeks, then took a job as ward maid at the St. Laurent Clinic, where she remained two months.

In March, 1945 the patient had erysipelas, which got better in a month. In April she resumed work for two months. In July a fresh attack of erysipelas confined her to bed completely until September, 1945. In September, 1945 a fresh return to work accompanied by a painful episode and a further increase in volume of the abdomen. At the end of two months, on November 6th, 1945, the patient hospitalized at Pontchaillou, St. Agnes Ward.

From November 6th, 1945 to January 31st, 1946 she stayed in St. Agnes. On January 31st the patient, having obtained a place in a sanatorium through the intervention of the out-patient department, went to Haut Lévêque (Gironde). She remained there up to April 24th, 1946. Her condition did not improve, and she was then placed in the Beune Ocean (Landes). She stayed there till December, 1946, the date when once again she entered Pontchaillou, St. Agnes Ward.

During her stay at Beune Ocean, from April to July, 1946, she thinks her general state did not improve. On July 9th, 1946, she had a surgical operation for bilateral hallux valgus and an attempt was made to correct the deformity of the feet with a plaster for three months. On July 16th the patient had a further operation on the upper jaw for closure of a fistula resulting from osteitis. This fistula had been present three and a half years, having appeared following an extraction of teeth. In August and in September two osseous curetages for osteitis of the superior maxilla at the right of the mid line.

Following these successive interventions the patient was very exhausted and lost weight. At the end of September, 1946 the patient had a haematemesis which recurred twice. Then for a month she had haematemesis every day. (Diagnosis of haematemesis confirmed by the sanatorium doctor.)

It is on account of the progressive worsening of her condition that the patient was admitted again to Pontchaillou.

During her final stay in Pontchaillou she appeared very ill indeed. Examined on December 9th, 1946, she was found to be tired, pale and losing weight, with an oscillating temperature of 103° F. to 95.7° F. morning and evening—higher in the morning. She had no appetite, suffered from night sweats and complained of continual abdominal pain. She vomited easily, at any time of day, and frequently after first vomiting food she would, a few minutes later, vomit blood. Her abdomen was greatly swollen, and on palpation a compact mass, not depressible but of doughy consistency, was apparent, stretching from costal margin to pubis and inguinal ligaments. Percussion revealed alternating areas of dullness and resonance over the whole abdomen. Examination of other parts revealed little of significance. X-rays of lungs were normal. It was said, 'From

the psychic point of view the patient seems to have a neuropathic tendency.'

In April, 1948 she had—'a very enlarged abdomen, the swelling spreading widely in the two iliac fossae and reaching up in
the form of a lump as far as the xiphoid process. On palpation it
is elastic, hard, can be depressed a little. It is tender in the left
iliac fossa and the umbilical region. The whole of this puffy
mass is resonant to percussion.'

Commencing April 16th, 1948 she was given streptomycin,
an antibiotic for tuberculous infections, and thereafter more or
less day-to-day notes were made. Her fever became if anything
worse and she had various functional disturbances—sweating,
noises in the ears, trembling attacks, no appetite, attacks of
vague shooting pains in the abdomen of no precise localization,
nausea, vomiting, dizziness, insomnia and headaches. Streptomycin was discontinued on May 29th. Thereafter her fever
became slowly and steadily more hectic until, just before her
departure for Lourdes, it was oscillating between 37° C. and
40° C. On July 30th there is a note: 'Pus in stools and vomit.'

This is the sum total of the medical information about the
nature of Jeanne Fretel's condition prior to her visit to Lourdes.
The diagnosis of tuberculous peritonitis, at least so far as these
notes go, rests entirely upon clinical impressions. The patient's
abdomen was opened about six times, but there is no mention
of any attempt to utilize these opportunities to confirm the
diagnosis by histological and bacteriological examination of
biopsy material. There is not even a description of the superficial appearance of the abdominal organs. At one stage an
ovary was removed, allegedly for tuberculous infection, but
there is no knowing whether the diagnosis was retrospective
or whether the organ was examined at the time and proved to
be infected. There is no report of any bacteriological examination of pus from her fistulae. There is no mention of any inoculation of fluid found in the abdomen at operation into a guinea
pig, although this test could have clinched the diagnosis of
tuberculosis.

The absence of any objective bacteriological evidence of
tuberculosis in a case in which—presuming the diagnosis to be

correct—such evidence could have been readily obtained strikes one as curious. It is not at all in conformity with modern medical practice to deal with a patient as a hopeless tuberculous invalid and to ignore all other possible diagnoses when no objective evidence of specific tuberculous infection is available.

Dr Debroise of Rennes, who took part in the examination of Jeanne Fretel at the Lourdes Medical Bureau, in a letter passed on to me by Colonel C. H. Green, endeavours to explain away the absence of diagnostic tests in the following terms:

In summary, this is what you can reply to Colonel Green who asks about the absence of a plate.

(I gather it is a question of the absence of a bacteriological examination of a smear from peritoneal fluid and not a matter of X-rays of the intestines. Actually such X-rays were taken, but as always showed nothing special; which is not surprising since it was a question of a peritoneal affection and not intestinal tuberculosis.)

In contrast to his American colleague, the French doctor is by temperament disposed to rely for diagnosis on clinical observation of the patient and on observation of the progress of the disease, rather than on laboratory tests. Now Jeanne Fretel had been in our hospital for some months. She had had five or six operations for abdominal troubles. Instead of being followed by normal healing, these interventions led to interminable scarring and fistula formation, as is the case in all tuberculous infection. For us, therefore, it was a serious abdominal affection having the characteristics of tuberculous peritonitis.

In addition, the patient was cachectic and in the stage of terminal unconsciousness, with meningitic reactions, and had stopped taking nourishment for a long time. She scarcely realized that she was being taken on a pilgrimage.

Apart from this, we know very well that a slide made with peritoneal fluid would not have shown us the T.B. bacillus, which is excessively rare in a peritoneal effusion. One could have done, in addition, a guinea pig inoculation.

But this examination, which is often chancy, only gives a result at the end of three months when the animal is sacrificed, and one is lucky if the guinea-pig has not died in the meantime of intercurrent disease.

It is obvious that such research luxuries are impractical during a stay in hospital, especially in the case of a patient whose demise is expected from one moment to the next. In private practice also, a slide for examination of peritoneal liquid is rarely prepared, and a guinea-pig injection is even more rarely carried out. Such procedures are reserved for patients with vague clinical signs, difficult to interpret without the help of a laboratory, and are not used for a patient whose

fate has been sealed by the failure of previous treatment and by con-
comitant hyperthermia and cachexia. In fact, a positive result in this
case would teach us nothing new, and a negative result would neither
change our diagnosis nor the patient's condition.

Carrel, whose scientific attitude cannot be questioned, pronounced
the word miracle and the diagnosis tuberculous peritonitis in the case
of Marie Branley, although he admitted that for mathematical certainty of diagnosis, a laparotomy, which was not actually done, would
have had to be performed. But the clinical history had forced upon him
the diagnosis without recourse to a slide.

Besides, does a miracle require mathematical certainty?

Finally, it must not be forgotten that we do not know in advance
which patient will be the object of the grace of a miraculous cure.
Only for that we could furnish him in advance with an unassailable
dossier. Would not that also be suspect?

If these statements do give a true picture of medical methods
in certain parts of France, one can only comment that it is highly
regrettable from the point of view of the investigator of unusual
cures—and perhaps even more regrettable from the point of
view of the sick patient.

On the information given no one could feel much confidence
in the diagnosis. Clinicians I consulted have pointed out
various diagnoses all of which would be consistent with the
history: (1) Infection originating from an appendicectomy,
leading to an appendix abscess followed by various operations
for 'adhesions' and the formation of fistulae. (2) Ulcerative
colitis, a condition in which the lower bowel becomes inflamed
and eroded. Psychosomatic influences are prominent in this
disease, but the sufferer can be desperately ill. (3) Actinomy-
cosis, which is another form of chronic infection not dissimilar
to tuberculosis, but caused by a fungus of microscopic dimen-
sions which is fortunately sensitive to penicillin. This disease
frequently attacks the intestine and causes fistulae which become secondarily infected by other bacteria so provoking suppuration and fever. Another favourite site for this infection is
the jaw, and it is noteworthy that Jeanne Fretel had had treatment for a jaw infection. (4) Chron's Disease, otherwise known
as regional ileitis, which is a localized inflammatory reaction in
the intestine leading to obstruction and other complications.
(5) Intestinal polyposis, that is the formation of small, plant-like

tumours on the lining of the intestine which bleed and cause obstruction.

As far as the notes go there is nothing to suggest that any of these possibilities was taken into consideration, let alone eliminated by microscopic tests. In view of the wide differences in treatment appropriate to these various conditions, an accurate diagnosis would have been of the greatest practical value. Few modern doctors would accept Dr Debroise's arguments against the use of laboratory tests. As for the supposed 'miracle', one's assessment naturally varies according to whether the patient really was suffering from widespread and long-standing tuberculosis, which would not be expected to yield suddenly to any form of treatment, or whether she had some relatively benign form of infection which the appropriate antibiotic might swiftly cure.

In an effort to find out whether by chance some objective observations had been made without finding their way into the available notes, I wrote first to Dr Pellé, who did not reply, and later to Dr George Desvaux, Mlle Fretel's own doctor. In a letter received from him in September, 1955 he promised to send me a copy of a medical report he was preparing on the case. In spite of reminders, up to the present time of writing, that is, December, 1956, no report has arrived. In his letter Dr Desvaux mentions that, according to the patient herself, tuberculous bacilli were found in her stools in January, 1946, during her stay in the Haut Lévêque sanatorium. If true, this finding would be inconsistent with Dr Debroise's statement that Jeanne Fretel had no intestinal tuberculosis. Dr Desvaux also states that the surgeon who operated in July, 1946 for bone infections of the foot and of the upper jaw declared the case tuberculous. This is contradictory to the hospital notes at Rennes, which state that the operation on the foot was to correct a congenital deformity—although why this should have been decided upon during a serious illness is not clear.

Without doubt tuberculous infection is a very probable diagnosis on the information given, but unfortunately it is not certain. The uncertainty is increased by the probable presence of a fairly large functional element suggested by features in the

history, by the plethora of functional reactions following streptomycin therapy, and by the mention in the hospital notes of
'neuropathic tendency'. In this connection it is interesting to
note that the fluctuations of temperature become really hectic
by about mid August, 1948. The medical certificate of application to go to Lourdes was signed by both Jeanne Fretel and
Dr Pellé on August 10th, 1948.

On the unsatisfactory, jumbled and occasionally inconsistent
information available no definite scientific statement can be
made about Jeanne Fretel's condition. She was apparently very
ill. At the Mass for the Sick the priest hesitated to give her
communion because she was so weak and vomiting constantly.
A few days later she was up and working. A 'miraculous transformation' certainly, but of what? Tuberculosis? Ulcerative
colitis? Or simply gross hysteria? Because the hospital records
are so incomplete and the Lourdes Bureau investigations so
superficial one cannot arrive at a certain conclusion. This case
seems potentially most remarkable; it is a tragedy that information is so lacking.

10. FRÄULEIN TRAUTE FULDA

When I was in Lourdes in the summer of 1955 this case,
which has since been pronounced miraculous, was still under
consideration by the ecclesiastical authorities and consequently
the dossier was not available. I have seen only the summary
which was sent to members of the Lourdes International Committee in January, 1955, and resulted in their decision to recom-
mend the case for consideration as miraculous. For this reason
it would be slightly unfair to come to a final conclusion about
this case since there is a possibility that the full dossier might
contain some additional piece of information that would put the
matter in a different light. I shall therefore give no more than
a brief sketch of the salient points.

In 1937, at the age of 23, Fräulein Fulda had a gastrectomy
operation for perforated stomach ulcer. Later that year she

developed an abscess on the kidney which was incised. The following year the right kidney was removed on account of pyonephritis caused by renal calculi.

After this second operation she developed asthenia, extreme lassitude and digestive troubles, and remained in a very poor general state. Her skin developed brown pigmentation, her blood pressure was low (80 and never exceeding 100) and she had a severe anaemia (red cells 2,900,000 with haemoglobin by Sahli method 42% in June, 1950). She was presumed to be suffering from insufficiency of the supra-renal glands (which are liable to be damaged in kidney operations) since weakness, low blood pressure and skin pigmentation are all features of this condition. When extracts of supra-renal cortex were administered by way of treatment for the deficiency her condition improved.

In spite of continuous hormone treatment, which could not be interrupted without the patient collapsing completely, Fräulein Fulda remained a chronic invalid, unable to get about except in a wheel chair and unable to sustain even slight muscular effort. In August, 1950 she visited Lourdes and suddenly improved—the circumstances of her recovery not being described in the summary—and was able to discontinue her hormone treatment. In the following months her weakness cleared up completely and the skin pigmentation subsided. Examined in 1951 and 1952, and given biochemical tests, she showed no signs of supra-renal disorder.

The obvious gap in this history is the absence of biochemical tests (17-ketosteroid estimations, Robinson's water elimination test, eosinophil response) which are generally regarded as necessary to establish the presence of supra-renal insufficiency. Dr Hans Siedek, who treated the patient and provided the chief medical reports, explains the gap as follows:

The diagnosis . . . was made in 1938 after some very exact metabolic examinations at the Hospital for Children (Institute for Scientific Research) in Vienna . . . Unfortunately these observations relating to the beginning of the illness have disappeared, in a singular manner it must be said, since all the other notes of illnesses are available. . . .

Here are the reasons why we did not carry out metabolic examinations before her departure for Lourdes. The diagnosis was certain and Fräulein Fulda was constantly under hormone treatment which could not be interrupted. The metabolism was therefore influenced by the treatment. Moreover, we did not envisage the possibility of a sudden cure and therefore we did not carry out the biochemical tests.

Whatever one thinks of Dr Siedek's explanations, the absence of this crucial evidence is regrettable for it means that an otherwise very remarkable case is capable of interpretation in terms of a functional starvation syndrome with secondary deficiency anaemia, a condition which might well respond to a dramatic change in attitude and habits. In support of this possibility it may be noted that such severe anaemia is not typical of supra-renal insufficiency, and that the skin pigmentation is not sufficiently described in the summary (whether restricted to exposed skin or present also inside the mouth) to be sure that it was of the type specifically associated with supra-renal disorder. Furthermore, if the illness was really due merely to supra-renal insufficiency, it seems curious that the hormone replacement treatment was not more effective in curing the patient.

11. MME COUTEAULT

Since this book was first completed Monseigneur Vion, Coadjutor Bishop of Poitiers, has announced that the cure of Mme Alice Couteault, which took place at Lourdes in May, 1952, has been declared miraculous by a diocesan canonical commission. Although I have not had the opportunity to study the complete dossier, I have a copy of the memorandum on the case circulated to members of the Lourdes International Medical Commission in January, 1955. The essential facts can be put quite briefly:

Mme Couteault, who was aged 34 at the time of her visit to Lourdes, had been ill three years. The trouble began with mild fever, weakness, pains around the hip joints radiating down the thighs, and the onset of stiffness of gait. In October, 1949 there

8

was a worsening of these symptoms, tendon reflexes became exaggerated and there was a 'paraplegic tendency', i.e. a tendency to spastic paralysis of the legs. At this stage the diagnosis of disseminated sclerosis was made.

Thereafter the condition worsened and there developed contractures of the legs, 'epileptoid tremors' of the feet, patellar clonus and spastic, inco-ordinate gait. From February to April, 1952 all these troubles worsened and Mme Couteault lost weight and appetite, had difficulty in passing urine and developed ulcerations on the soles of her feet. Her husband testified that she had great tremulousness and clumsiness in her hand movements and a loss of her sense of balance which forced her to drag about with her two chairs in order to stop herself from falling. After Easter, 1952 her husband had to carry her upstairs and help her to undress.

In May, 1952 Mme Couteault was taken to Lourdes and during the period May 12th to May 16th she improved steadily so that finally she was able to get off her stretcher and present herself at the Lourdes Bureau. There the doctors could observe no abnormality of gait, no contractures of the legs and no clonus. She had normal knee jerks and pupillary responses, but she retained a trace of vertical nystagmus and an exaggerated right ankle jerk accompanied by 'epileptoid tremor'. On her return home her doctor confirmed these findings. The patient's health steadily improved. Her chronic fever disappeared, she resumed normal activities and she gained weight. A careful medical examination in 1954 confirmed that she maintained good health. The only residual signs of her illness were 'pyramidal signs'— vigorous reflexes and a trace of clonus.

This case merits but brief comment for, medically speaking, it ranks as one of the least interesting miracles. Disseminated sclerosis is a patchy, degenerative disease of the nervous system of very varied symptomatology, course and outcome. No effective treatment is known to combat the degenerative process, but spontaneous permanent recovery is not rare and remissions lasting years are not uncommon. Since the underlying cause is so obscure, the diagnosis is more of a label than an exact scientific concept, and it may well cover a whole variety of pathological processes, some more serious than others. As in other cases, the striking feature is not so much the almost complete recovery as the swiftness of the transition from severe invalidism to only slight incapacity in the space of four days. As usual one would like to know the exact physical state immediately before her visit to Lourdes. The medical evidence shows she suffered from organic paralysis of spastic type in 1949 and 1950, but was this paralysis still present in May, 1952, or was her invalidism due to nothing more than the functional aftermath of a past physical disorder? In the summary available to me I can find no record of a neurological examination shortly before the cure, so the question remains unanswerable.

The account of the eleven miracle cases is now complete. For ease of reference here is the list of diagnoses:

Name	Visited Lourdes	Diagnosis
Mlle Gabrielle Clauzel	1941	Spinal arthritis
Mme Gestas	1946–7	Post-gastrectomy disturbances
Mme Rose Martin	1947	Secondary cancer
Francis Pascal	1938	Paralysis from meningitis
Colonel Pellegrin	1950	Fistula
Sister Marguerite	—	Nephritis
Mlle Thérèse Canin	1947	Peritoneal Tuberculosis
Mlle Louise Jamain	1937	Pulmonary Tuberculosis
Mlle Jeanne Fretel	1948	Peritoneal Tuberculosis
Fräulein Fulda	1950	Addison's Disease
Mme Couteault	1952	Disseminated Sclerosis

In no case was the evidence really satisfactory, and in certain cases the evidence suggested a perfectly natural alternative explanation. Thus Mlle Clauzel's symptoms were apparently largely functional and her organic condition (such as it was) remained uninfluenced by her symptomatic relief. Mme Martin, who was supposed to be suffering from a cancer, might instead have been suffering from severe obstructive constipation due to her addiction to morphia. The healing of Colonel Pellegrin's fistula would scarcely have provided material for discussion had it not happened to take place about the time of his Lourdes visit. Likewise Mme Gestas, who appears to have been suffering from a self-limiting dumping syndrome, might well have got better just as easily if she had never heard of Lourdes. Francis Pascal's partial recovery of sight is perhaps the most puzzling case, although the possibility of such a recovery depends on what interpretation is put upon the uncertain diagnosis. As for Traute Fulda's so-called Addison's Disease, the diagnosis is too uncertain to form a judgment, and the same might be said of both Mlle Canin's and Mlle Fretel's supposed tuberculous peritonitis. In only one case were full hospital records including laboratory tests and X-rays available both before and after the cure. That was Louise Jamain whose X-rays were normal to start with! The case of Sister Marie Marguerite is the only one in which the events—if true—merit the adjective miraculous, and in this case the medical evidence is conspicuously absent.

V

THE CURES IN GENERAL

(1) THE PREDOMINANCE OF TUBERCULOSIS

THE official 'miracles' represent only a small minority of the
cases accepted by the Lourdes Bureau as genuine instances
of remarkable cures. A consideration of this larger population
of cases might reveal some general trends that are not apparent
among the eleven miracle cures.

In the appendix appears a list of cures compiled from published sources. All of these were accepted by the Lourdes
Medical Bureau in the period 1925 to 1950. More recent cures
are not listed because some years have to elapse before published
records become available. There are ninety-eight cases in all,
each with a diagnosis.

Some interesting points are immediately apparent. As already
remarked, the great majority of the cures are of internal diseases of long-standing. There are no self-evident 'miracles',
such as the regeneration of lost eyes or amputated fingers. Over
half of the cures in the list (fifty) were cures of some form of
tuberculosis. Only three were cures of malignant cancers.
Since tuberculosis frequently recovers spontaneously, but malignant disease rarely does, these figures are in conformity with
natural interpretations. But it is curious that there should be
such a high proportion of tuberculosis cases. It hardly seems
likely that there could be such an abnormally high proportion
of cases of tuberculosis among the sick who visit Lourdes; it
looks as if the tuberculosis cases are singled out for cure in
preference to other diseases. Is this because Lourdes has a
particularly beneficial effect upon tuberculosis sufferers or is it
because the label 'tuberculosis' is wrongly used for cases of
functional debility that respond to suggestion? The answer cannot be more than speculative, but I think there is some evidence
for both explanations.

First, only five of these cures of tuberculosis were cures of males, four-fifths were females. This reflects the general preponderance of females among the persons cured. Three-quarters are females in the present list. Since hysterical disorders of function are commoner in women, this is a small point in favour of the hypothesis of a large functional element in many cases. Second, we have the study of cures of pulmonary tuberculosis at Lourdes by the Catholic specialist, Dr W. Jullien. He finds that in the majority of the alleged cures the evidence necessary to form a firm diagnosis (contemporary X-rays and microsopic examinations and/or cultures) is lacking. Nevertheless, there were some cases he was able to accept—Louise Jamain, who has already been discussed, Madeleine Guinot, quoted in Dr Anicet Guarner's thesis (13), and Mlle Emilie Cailleux, quoted in Dr Henry Monnier's thesis (32).

Dr Ferron, in his thesis on Lourdes, takes a more sceptical view. He writes (11, p. 34): 'Up to 1910, that is to say before the routine use of chest X-rays, a third and sometimes even a half of the Lourdes miracles were cases of pulmonary tuberculosis. Today this proportion is considerably reduced. Formerly cure used to be assessed on the basis of subjective phenomena and sometimes on auscultatory signs. Today X-rays are demanded. We know now that pulmonary tuberculosis evolves in small steps under the influence of the nervous, vasometer and hormonal systems. That these advances of the disease have been arrested at Lourdes is an indisputable fact. It is even possible that complete cures begin in this fashion. In contrast, there is no indisputable proof of instantaneous healing of tuberculous lesions.'

In her critical thesis on Lourdes cures, Mme Thérèse Valot (44) discusses the diagnoses of Pott's Disease (tuberculosis of the spine) and tuberculous peritonitis, both of which occur frequently in the Lourdes Bureau's list of cures. Cures of Pott's Disease were commoner in years gone by, and Mme Valot attributes this to increasing efficiency in the elimination of misdiagnoses. Previous to the work of Dr Sorrel, many cases of non-tuberculous vertebral epiphysitis in young people (Scheuermann's Disease), which is an affection with a relatively benign

course and favourable outcome, were mistakenly put down as
Pott's Disease. Dr Roger Ferron makes the same point in his
thesis (11). Mme Valot quotes in illustration two alleged cures
of Pott's Disease registered by the Lourdes Bureau in the period
1930–32. In the first case the radiologist's report stated that the
X-ray showed no lesion of the vertebral bodies, but a certain
infiltration of the surrounding tissues. In the second case an
X-ray report before the cure stated: 'No necrotic lesions, no
loss of substance or collapse of the vertebrae, but a zone of decalcification of limited extent.' In the absence of signs of bone
erosion, or narrowing of the spaces between the vertebrae, the
definite opinion that tuberculosis was present seems unjustified.
Mme Valot notes that in spite of this uncertainty the Lourdes
Bureau describes the first of these cases as 'generalized tuberculous infection' (*Annales de Notre Dame de Lourdes*. April,
1934).

The frequency of alleged cures of tuberculous peritonitis
Mme Valot attributes to the inherent variability of the course of
this disease and the known possibility of sudden, spontaneous
recovery without treatment. She refers to two cases mentioned
by Professor Perrault which had nothing to do with Lourdes,
but which were as remarkable as any claimed by the Bureau.
One of these was a man of 35 who was in hospital with severe
tuberculous peritonitis accompanied by intractable fever and
vomiting of blood. Opening up the abdomen by a laparotomy
operation had failed to help. When the city of Paris was
liberated during the war, this patient suddenly got up and left
hospital without permission, joined the army, fought successfully, and returned in perfect health. In such cases one suspects
that the severity of the disturbance comes less from the amount
and virulence of the infecting bacteria than from the patient's
abnormally sensitive reactions.

A reasonable evaluation of the position would be as follows.
Inadequate diagnostic criteria and the inclusion of cases with a
large functional element lead to greatly exaggerated claims for
cures of tuberculosis at Lourdes. Nevertheless a certain resi-
duum of cases suggests that sometimes a visit to Lourdes has a
substantial beneficial effect upon the course of the illness. Such

an observation fits in with the modern tendency to regard tuberculosis and similar ailments as partly psychosomatic and in some cases susceptible to psychological influences. It is not unreasonable to suppose that the powerful impact of a pilgrimage to Lourdes might sometimes suffice to stimulate an unexpected recovery. How this can work out in practice Dr Jullien describes in detail in the case of the Abbé D. who happened to be one of his own patients (16).

The Abbé came under treatment in July, 1928. X-rays showed symmetrical lesions in the upper thirds of both lung fields which appeared as very dense confluent spots of crumbly appearance at the level of the clavicles. On auscultation there were no adventitious sounds, there was very slight dullness posteriorly at the level of the two apices and broncho-vesicular breathing. Temperature varied between 99.6° F. in the morning and 100.4° F. to 100.6° F. at 5 p.m. Dr Jullien collapsed the right upper lobe by a pneumothorax, leaving the two healthy lower lobes functioning.

The Abbé's symptoms were more severe than seemed warranted by the amount of disease. He had no appetite at all, and was losing weight rapidly (7 st. 13 lb.). He appeared breathless on the slightest movement, he could not speak aloud, complained of numerous pains, he had to be supported if he left his bed, and he was generally depressed, sensitive and fearful.

The Abbé visited Lourdes on September 16th, and after immersion felt immediately better, recovered his voice and his appetite and was able to walk about and dress himself. Dr Jullien saw him on September 20th—'a changed man, energetic . . . no longer coughed or spat, felt perfectly well, ate with a tremendous appetite . . . convinced he was completely cured'. But the X-ray picture taken the same day showed exactly the same diseased appearance as previously. Dr Jullien therefore continued with the pneumothorax. The patient's feeling of well-being and good appetite continued—in spite of an oscillating fever of 100° F. in the morning to 101° F. in the evening and a right pleural effusion. He proceeded to a complete recovery, gained over five stones in weight, and subsequently maintained good health.

This case shows that a sudden and enormous improvement in subjective symptoms does not necessarily signify a correspondingly immediate change in physical state. Nevertheless, in cases such as that of the Abbé D., it seems likely that the Lourdes influence was ultimately responsible for the recovery, but the effect is neither instantaneous nor miraculous.

(2) THE RELIABILITY OF THE DOCUMENTS

Before describing any of the cures I explained that I intended to take the documents at their face value and not to attempt to subject the recorded testimony to the exacting scrutiny that students of psychical research customarily apply to evidence for allegedly supernormal happenings. Nevertheless it has been impossible to avoid making some elementary observations that have a bearing upon the question of the trustworthiness or otherwise of the documents upon which the Lourdes evidence is founded.

Some indications have been given already in the course of discussions on particular cases. A certain carelessness in presentation, which would never be tolerated in a teaching hospital, pervades all the material. Incompleteness of data and lack of consideration of alternative diagnoses are the worst faults. An extreme bias in the matter of interpretation shows itself from time to time, as for instance in the case of Mlle Clauzel, in which the Lourdes doctors refused to recognize obvious symptoms of hysteria and resolutely asserted that a purely subjective improvement in a relatively mild spinal arthritis constituted a miracle. Bias in interpretation could go together with scrupulous fairness in the statement of facts, but it is unlikely. In this same case of Mlle Clauzel, the fact that a psychiatric consultation had taken place was not stated although it must have been known. In the case of Francis Pascal, the blind boy, some pertinent criticisms by Dr Charpin and Dr Latil which were included in the full dossier were suppressed in the published version of the cure. In the case of Rose Martin, the crucial fact that she had

had an abnormal bowel movement was explicitly denied, although evidence to this effect was to be found in the dossier itself. These are no more than chance indications picked up by noting internal inconsistencies. One wonders what other distortions, suppressions and mis-statements might not be discovered were it possible to compare all the official dossiers with some independent source of information. Unfortunately it has been possible to do this in only two cases, but with extremely interesting results in both instances.

The first case in question is the cure of the Abbé D., which has just been described in the discussion on tuberculosis.

The case was published in some detail by Dr Vallet when he was president of the Lourdes Bureau, and it is possible to compare the official Lourdes Bureau version with the independent but sympathetic account by Dr Jullien, the specialist in charge of the case.

According to Dr Jullien the Abbé had 'a modest attack of the upper third of the two lungs'.

According to the Lourdes Medical Bureau, however, he had 'bilateral pulmonary infection developing in the form of acute miliary tuberculosis'. Neither the X-rays nor the type of fever support such a diagnosis. It is as if the Lourdes doctors had said to themselves: 'This man had been very ill, therefore he must have had the disease in its gravest form.' The Lourdes Bureau accepts the cure as instantaneous and complete in spite of the fact that the X-ray and auscultatory signs were unchanged and the patient soon after began to suffer from pleural effusion! They also ignore the fact that Dr Jullien's treatment by pneumothorax had arrested the loss of weight (and therefore presumably brought about some improvement) before ever the Abbé visited Lourdes. Their clinical observations are equally odd.

September 18th, 1928: 'Right lung: The organ expands with difficulty. In front in the upper third, the sub-clavicular region, there are signs of fibrosis.'

In point of fact, the patient did not have a healed and fibrosed upper third of lung but an upper third collapsed by pneumothorax.

In the version of this case published by Dr Vallet, past-President of the Lourdes Medical Bureau, in his book, *Guérisons de Lourdes en* 1927–29 (41), these discrepancies are completely suppressed. Far from admitting any error Dr Vallet sticks obstinately to his opinion that the Abbé was gravely ill from acute miliary tuberculosis and that the cure was miraculous. He explains that the diagnosis of miliary tuberculosis was based on the total constellation of symptoms which supplemented the physical signs and, by their severity, showed the gravity of the pulmonary lesion. He points out that disproportionate severity of symptoms compared with mildness of physical signs is a feature of the miliary form of tuberculosis. Considering that miliary tuberculosis does produce characteristic signs on the X-ray and also a typical fever, neither of which were present, and considering that the history of a slow developing pulmonary lesion does not at all suggest the acute miliary form of the disease, Dr Vallet's arguments simply reveal the extent of his own will to believe. He absolutely refused to acknowledge the obvious explanation of the Abbé's exaggerated symptoms, in spite of Dr Jullien's testimony as to the patient's anxiety state.

In the face of this demonstrable instance of inefficiency and biased exaggeration, one cannot help but view with increased scepticism the many records in which there is no independent specialist like Dr Jullien to check the Lourdes Bureau version.

There is one other case, a more recent one, that of the blind boy Gérard Baillie, in which I have been able, through the kind help of Dr Paul Vasse of Amiens, to secure independent information about a Lourdes cure. This case does not feature among the official miracles. Having been passed by the Lourdes doctors it was rejected by a Canonical Commission on the ground that sight was not perfectly restored. But the case is described in glowing terms in Leuret's book, it is frequently cited as an inexplicable cure, for instance by Dr Leslie Weatherhead (46) and Dr Ruth Cranston (8), and it is often quoted as an example of the extreme stringency of the Church's requirements in regard to miraculous cures.

The version of the case published by Leuret and Bon (22) is as follows. The sections in square brackets I have summarized:

[Following the administration of an anaesthetic for a hernia operation at the age of 2, Gérard's sight deteriorated, and by the age of 2½ he was blind. He was suffering from bilateral chorio-retinitis, an incurable degenerative condition. He was put into an Institution for Blind Children on the certificate of Mrs. Biziaut, an ophthalmologist, who stated: 'Double optic atrophy. Incurable blindness.' In September, 1947, after two years in the institution, where none questioned the genuineness of his blindness, he was brought to Lourdes. He was then 4½. On the fourth day of the pilgrimage, while climbing the rough and rocky way of the Cross of Calvary, led by the hand by his mother, he suddenly saw his mother and exclaimed, 'Mamma, you have a pretty dress.'] Dr Leuret continues:

We examined him in the evening. He could see, but his vision was peculiar; as if he was looking through two separate tubes, which did not seem to permit unified vision, nor an appreciation of perspective, but *he could see*: he could take a watch into his hand, and point out with his finger various neighbouring objects. But after the next day he could see well and see everything. In the dormitory of the Asile de N.D. des Sept Douleurs he ran about and jumped from one bed to another; he entered the lift and pressed all the buttons. We took him to an excellent ophthalmologist at Tarbes, Dr Camps, one-time pupil at the Quatre Vingts National College of Ophthalmology (which is in itself a reference). This doctor, sceptical at first, with an admirable professional conscience gave him a prolonged examination and finished by saying to us: 'This is a child with bilateral chorio-retinitis and double optic atrophy; he cannot see and he ought not to be able to see.' Now, in fact he could see—admittedly he saw imperfectly, as if across a grating, but he could see.

On returning by car on the road to Lourdes he saw the mountains, and on this particular day, as though the Good Lord wanted to give the child, whose vision had just been reborn, a splendid view of the magnificence of creation, the mountains under a light covering of snow glistened in the sun's rays, and the child enthusiastically clapped his hands and shouted: 'Mamma, what is it? What is that?' It was necessary to explain to him what were the mountains, the snow, the sun, etc.

[He returned from Lourdes to the Institution, but was soon discharged because he could now see. He joined a normal school two miles away from home and was able to make his own way there and back on foot and take part in the lessons, both reading and writing, although his visual acuity was only 2/10 or 3/10.]

He returned to Lourdes the following year. He was re-examined by Dr Smith of Glasgow, an ophthalmologist of repute, who gave him a prolonged examination and came to the same diagnosis as had Dr Camps the preceding year: 'This child has a bilateral chorio-retinitis with double optic atrophy. He should not be able to see. But he does see.'

[The case gave rise to considerable discussion. The National Medical Commission decided] 'to obtain further expert opinion, and the matter was placed in the hands of Dr Lescault, ophthalmologist to the Lille Hospitals, who examined Gérard Baillie once again. The result of this expert examination was, to say the least, unexpected. Dr Lescault pronounced as follows: 'It does not appear disputable that Gérard Baillie had a bilateral chorio-retinitis, with double optic atrophy. But at present, *he has them no longer.* A cure of chorio-retinitis with optic atrophy is something *I have never seen.*' There are therefore two consecutive events, the one as extraordinary as the other.

In the first place, a child who, over a period of nearly two years, *sees* without being able to see, because all the visual organs were destroyed. He was in the same situation as a camera taking photos without films or plates.

In the second place, the reconstruction of a retina that was destroyed and an optic nerve that was atrophied two years before, is something that I have never seen; although in exceptional cases one sees a re-generation of the optic nerve after three or four months of atrophy when a cerebral tumour has been operated on early, one never sees an optic nerve regenerate after two years of atrophy, and especially not in a case of infective chorio-retinitis.

This case illustrates magnificently what has been pointed out before: The Holy Virgin acts as if she wanted to produce her own medical evidence. For two years all the medical observations which took place proved again and again that Gérard Baillie had a bilateral chorio-retinitis with optic atrophy, and when these observations had been effected, and no possible doubt remained, *the child was cured.*

As described, the case seems most impressive, but the account bristles with inaccuracies and suppressions. As re-corded on the Lourdes record form itself, Gérard Baillie was born on March 19th, 1939, so he was 8½ and not 4½ at the time of his visit to Lourdes. Dr Godéchoux, an ophthalmologist at Amiens (a Roman Catholic doctor who concerns himself with Lourdes pilgrimages and whose name appears in connection with other cases), examined Gérard Baillie on several occasions, as Dr Leuret had requested him to provide the boy with spec-tacles. Dr Paul Vasse, a member of the Society for Psychical Research who lives at Amiens, kindly made personal contact with Dr Godéchoux and secured his version of the case, which differs in important respects from that given in Leuret's book. According to Dr Godéchoux, the condition was not consequent upon poisoning by an anaesthetic, for the child had never been able to see properly, and the parents had noticed the disability when he was only eighteen months of age. More particularly, Dr Godéchoux disagrees very much with the opinion attributed to Dr Lescaux that 'Baillie had a bilateral chorio-retinitis, with double optic atrophy, but now *he has them no longer*'.

Dr Godéchoux's written report of his examination, dated Amiens, September 20th, 1950, is preserved in the Lourdes files and is duplicated in his correspondence with Dr Vasse. His main findings were:

Divergent strabismus of the left eye. Slight vertical nystagmiform movements of the globes. Pupillary reactions to light and accommodation very feeble. In the fundus, on each side discrete pigmentations distributed over the whole of the retina. Disc a waxy complexion with edges indistinct. Arteries filiform, but veins of normal calibre. Visual fields certainly very constricted, but impossible to measure. Movements hesitant, the child picks his way across the room. Night blindness. Visual acuity, not improved by lenses, 1/10 in each eye. Reads No. 2 on the Parinaud scale, which corresponds to the small letters of a newspaper.[1]
Conclusion: Baillie suffers from a retinal sclerosis with discrete pigmentatory formation. Retinitis pigmentosa.

From this description, three years after the 'cure', Baillie's eyes were in such a bad state one wonders whether any substantial change really took place at Lourdes. But what of Dr Lescaux's examination? Fortunately his full report is still available in the Lourdes files:

Extracts from Dr Lescaux's Report

Examination. To begin with there is a divergent strabismus, apparently alternating, but predominantly on the left eye. Also certain constant movements. The external appearance of the eyes is normal.
Before any examination in the dark room, I made the child read like an ordinary child patient and I obtained the visual acuity.
Right eye without lenses. 1/6 (Scale of Weiker).
Left eye without lenses 1/10.

[1] In later examinations he did not do so well on this test—D.J.W.

He read at 15 cm. distance the text for 1/10, but read the figures better, liking arithmetic particularly.

In the dark room. Ophthalmoscopic examination under atropine. Right and left eyes. No trouble in the transparent media.

Optic discs. Clearly coloured, showing no discoloration from optic atrophy, not even partial.

The retina has not the usual clearness. It shows a diffuse brownish tint, but without the true lesions of pigmentatory choroiditis, not even peripherally. (Examination in spite of considerable difficulty due to slight ocular tremor with nystagmoid movements.) It is an atypical fundus, but one which does not allow of a classical diagnostic label.

Refraction shows a slight hypermetropia, but attempts at correction under atropine lead to no modification of the visual acuity.

To-day: ophthalmological findings are much closer to those which have been found since his first journey to Lourdes than they are to those given in the certificates prior to his pilgrimage.

Although it cannot be determined exactly, on account of the child's age, the visual field as estimated by movements of the hand shows a concentric, bilateral constriction.

Discussion

There is one indisputable fact that is public knowledge. Since his journey to Lourdes this child shows a *functional improvement surpassing both the prognostic indications* and the hopes of his parents, and this improvement seems to be continuing, both in the right and in the left eye.

To take up one point—in some correspondence from Dr Delogé (of Nice) which features in the dossier—I am in agreement with him when he explains that vision is at the same time both physical and psychical. It is probable in this child's case that a psychical shock could have produced this regular improvement of visual acuity, this awakening of ocular sensibility to the limits that we observe today.

Furthermore, perhaps the child's increasing maturity allows him to appreciate his visual acuity better now than when he was two or three years of age.

Conclusion. Until further observations can be made later, it seems sufficient to declare here that we have *an unhoped-for improvement of visual acuity*, a very appreciable improvement, although not total, in spite of modifications in the optic disc, which has regained colour and lost its atrophic appearance, a phenomenon which I have never before observed.

(Signed) Lescaux.

It is quite clear from this that the sentence given in Dr Leuret's book, which I can find nowhere in Dr Lescaux's report, gives a very exaggerated picture of the specialist's opinion. Dr Lescaux concludes that there has been 'a very appreciable improvement', but prudently advises 'further observations later'. The major point of difference between his observations and those of Dr Godéchoux is in the description of the optic discs. Dr Lescaux describes them as having regained their normal colour. Since Dr Godéchoux had the opportunity to examine Gérard Baillie on several occasions, the last time in March, 1953, his views carry greater weight. Dr Lescaux also cites the cautionary remarks that Dr Charles Delogé wrote to Dr Leuret. The Canonical Commission report also cites Dr Delogé as follows:

In the first place, it is not a matter of a purely *organic* illness. The observations by Dr Ch. Delogé, one-time ophthalmological assistant to the Paris Hospitals, and oculist to the Monaco Hospital, have attracted the attention of the Commission.
'In spite of some opinions,' he writes in his letter of August 29th, 1948, 'vision is at the same time physical and psychical. This is very important and if I insist upon the point it is because nobody, or almost nobody, takes the fact into account.' And this specialist cited a case that well illustrated his opinion on this matter.

Dr Delogé was by no means the only person to caution Dr Leuret, as is shown by the following quotations from letters in the Lourdes files:

In accordance with what had been requested of me, I took this child to the ophthalmological clinic at Lille and showed him to the specialist without explaining about the events at Lourdes.
Dr Delogé concluded that the child had very poor sight, difficult to improve, and proposed hospitalization for a complete examination.
I did not want to leave Gérard at the hospital because his parents did not wish it. They believe that a miracle has happened, and they do not care whether it is recognized or not. . . .

Extract from a letter to
Dr Leuret from Dr Boury, dated September 9th, 1948

There are, especially nowadays, many children in institutions who can see quite clearly. Officially, they must have less than 1/20 vision, but many have 1/10 and even more. In all blind schools there are children who can read in the dark; they learn braille only as a precaution, because their sight is not very strong, because there is reason to fear blindness some time in the future, or because it is advisable to avoid straining such feeble powers as they possess.

I would be inclined to modify the phrase 'which abundantly proves that, blind when he set out, he saw clearly when he returned . . .'

Thus, Dr Leuret's published version omits all mention of several important residual defects—nystagmus, squint and feeble pupillary reflexes. He selects a particular point from Dr Lescaux's report about the disappearance of pallor due to optic atrophy, but omits all mention of Dr Lescaux's remarks about improvement perhaps being due to the child growing up to make better practical use of his defective vision. He also fails to mention that Dr Godéchoux disagreed over the matter of optic atrophy, and that Dr Godéchoux examined the child several times. He ignores the cautions and criticisms of his own colleagues. As for Dr Smith, the English authority who was quoted, Colonel Charles Green tells me he has traced him, that he has become a monk, and that he now says that he was not at all impressed by the case of Gérard Baillie. No written statement from Dr Smith is available, but as Colonel Green is a Roman Catholic and has written a book on Lourdes from the standpoint of an enthusiastic believer I have no reason to doubt his evidence.

The case of the Abbé D. and that of Gérard Baillie cast such doubt upon the objectivity of Lourdes Bureau officials that one is forced to scrutinize all their claims with some scepticism.

(3) CANCER CURES

To return to the matter of the types of illness reported to be cured, I have already remarked upon the very small number of cancer recoveries claimed in modern times. I have discovered only three. One of these, the case of Mme Martin, has already been discussed as one of the official miracles. In that case the diagnosis was, to say the least, open to doubt.

The second case is that of Mlle Delot, who was said to have been cured of a malignant tumour of the pylorus when she visited Lourdes in 1926. Dr Robert Leroy gives an account of the case, and some discussion (21). It also features among the collection in Dr Vallet's *La Verité sur Lourdes* (43), and in the book by Boissarie de l'Épine (6). For many months Mlle Delot had been suffering from stomach pains and loss of weight and appetite, and for two months she had been passing blood in the stools and vomiting back her food. In November, 1925 an X-ray showed a definite ulcerous crater of the stomach wall in the pre-pyloric region. Dr Houzel, a surgeon, certifies that in November, 1925 he operated upon the patient, found an inoperable tumour obstructing the pyloric opening, and therefore performed a gastro-enterostomy which would give temporary relief by permitting food to bypass the obstruction.

Four months later, in April, 1926, pains recurred and her medical man, Dr Vallois, found a large mass in the abdomen, which formed an integral part of the operation scar, as well as an enlargement of the liver, which protruded 3 cm. below the costal margin and showed the characteristic nodules of secondary cancer. Mlle Delot's condition worsened, and vomiting and intolerance of food returned.

She visited Lourdes, bathed on July 31st, 1926, and felt suddenly better and hungry. Next day she visited the Lourdes Medical Bureau, where the doctors were divided in their opinions. She was told to come back a year later. On August 26th, 1926 she was examined again by Dr Vallois, who could no longer find any trace of a palpable tumour, enlarged liver or cancerous nodules. X-rays on August 20th and 21st, 1926 by Dr Cherfils revealed 'Stomach hypotonic and very elongated. Marked ptosis of the transverse. Slight delay in emptying of the stomach.' Also, there was no sign of the gastro-enterostomy. Mlle Delot regained weight rapidly and in a letter dated February, 1943, seventeen years after her cure, she stated she was still enjoying perfect health.

The most curious point, however, is that X-rays taken in 1928 not only revealed normal vigorous stomach movements with no trace of ulcer, tumour or obstruction, but there was likewise no trace of the gastro-enterostomy said to have been performed by Dr Houzel. Dr Leroy comments: 'I am well aware of the fact that a gastro-enterostomy can no longer function if the pylorus becomes permeable again. But the X-ray report insists: 'The peristaltic wave travels through the whole of the greater curvature without any stop, and palpation completely dissociates the wall of the stomach from any neighbouring intestinal loop without any barium mouthful ever passing other than through the pylorus.' Dr Leroy points out that it would be necessary to grant that the miracle not only caused the disappearance of the tumour but also modified the anatomy of the organs, eliminating the opening made by the surgeon and replacing it with a new piece of intestinal wall. His only comment is, '. . .'. No wonder the 'cure' aroused controversy in the medical bodies. Perhaps it is simplest to doubt the surgeon's word. Mme Valot points out that such discrepancies are not so unusual as one might suppose. When she was working in a department of radiology, she came across in a single month two patients, both of whom had had abdominal operations believed to be gastro-enterostomy without any sign of it appearing on their X-rays (44, p. 65).

Has this case been uncomplicated by conflict between the surgical and radiological evidence, one might have been tempted to grant a clear-cut cancer cure. No mention is made of any pathological examination of the tumour material, but on purely clinical grounds—if one can accept the testimony—the diagnosis would seem to have been all too obvious. Nevertheless there is room for doubt, as shown by discussions published in the November, 1928 Bulletin of the International Medical Association of Lourdes in which such alternative diagnoses as 'peri-gastritis with peritoneal thickenings' and 'hypertrophic tuberculosis' were put forward. However, it is a relatively old case, and I have not had the opportunity to follow up the details, as was done in the matter of Gérard Baillie, so I prefer to suspend judgment. It is worth pointing out that in this cure, as in so many others, there seems to be a considerable time gap between the date of the 'cure' and the last recorded medical examination, so the instantaneousness of the cure cannot be taken as substantiated. Mlle Delot was unfortunately killed in the bombardment of Boulogne in 1944 so the possibility of exploring further by post-mortem examination does not arise.

The third example of malignancy is a case of Hodgkin's

Disease. I have the details from the account circulated to members of the Lourdes International Medical Commission, which the President, Dr Grenet, kindly allowed me to see. The case was described by Professor J. Lhermitte at a public meeting in Paris on February 15th, 1955. As the case is relatively recent, and as far as I know unpublished, I shall refer to the patient as Signor G.

Signor G. was admitted to hospital in January, 1950. Two weeks of general malaise ushered in a fever, varying from 37° C. in the morning to 40° C. in the evening, which persisted in spite of treatment with penicillin. A blood serum test had at first been positive for paratyphoid A, but was later negative. On admission his spleen was found to be enlarged and a blood examination showed a great reduction in white cells.

Red cells: 4,300,000/ml.

White cells: 1,400/ml.

neutrophils—54%	lymphocytes—30%
eosinophils—2%	monocytes—14%

On January 10th he was found to have two swollen glands in the left axilla, they were hard, painless and mobile, and the size of a haricot bean.

Treatment with penicillin and aureomycin failed to bring down the temperature, and the patient got worse. On February 16th the glands were excised for histological examination. The first specialist to examine the preparations was uncertain, two others thought they showed Hodgkin's Disease. Accordingly the patient was given mustard derivatives—phenylbutazol— later combined with deep X-rays to the axilla, but without improvement. More glands appeared in the left axilla and the enlargement of the spleen increased slightly. On March 25th the patient went home, where he had numerous blood transfusions. Still weak and suffering from fever he was taken to Lourdes on May 31st, 1950 where, after his first bath, he suddenly felt better and was very soon able to get up and take part in pilgrimage duties. Examined at the Lourdes Bureau four years later (August 16th, 1954) he was in good health, although they found palpable glands in the left cervical and sub-clavicular regions.

This medical history is peculiar. The original diagnosis of paratyphoid A seems reasonable, and is consistent with the insidious onset, the low white cell count, the fever, the initial agglutination test result, the enlarged spleen and the failure to respond to aureomycin and penicillin, which are ineffective in this infection. The persistence of fever and low white cell count is puzzling, but could conceivably be due to the noxious agents used in this treatment.

The diagnosis of Hodgkin's Disease (a sort of cancer of the lymph glands) by histological means is often very difficult, and in this case the experts were not all agreed. In criticizing this case Dr Valot quotes the observations of Professor W. Berardinelli who sent biopsy specimens from the same benign case to four reputable histological authorities and got back three diagnoses of malignant Hodgkin's Disease confirmed by the presence of Sternberg cells (44, p. 88). Apart from the uncertainty of the histological evidence, a severe and selective reduction in the white blood cells, such as was reported in this case, is not typical of Hodgkin's Disease, although according to Price's *Textbook of the Practice of Medicine* it may occur together with a typhoid-like fever in severe and rapidly progressive cases. Altogether it is difficult to come to any firm conclusion. The swollen glands could have been a red-herring—witness the fact that he had a few in 1954 when he was perfectly well. On the other hand he might have had Hodgkin's Disease and recovered either spontaneously or as a result of treatment, both of which are known possibilities. Remissions of five years or even longer are relatively common.

Thus, of the three malignancy cases I have found, Rose Martin's can be readily explained in other ways, Signor G.'s is open to various interpretations, and the most clear-cut case, that of Mlle Delot, is suspect on account of contradictory evidence. In short, there is scant evidence from these three cases that Lourdes has any significant effect upon the course of malignant disease.

In case any reader may think that the Lourdes evidence has

been unfairly treated by the omission of all the old cases of
alleged cancer cures, it is worth mentioning that, with the ex-
ception of Signor G., whose diagnosis is doubtful, in no case
ever has microscopical evidence been produced to confirm the
diagnosis, although such evidence is habitually called for in
current medical practice. The cases that have been put forward
as cancer cures often concern supposed recurrences of cancers
that have previously been treated with surgery. So it was with
Mme Rose Martin, and so it was with Catherine Lapeyre, whose
case is frequently quoted—e.g. by de Grandmaison and by Le
Bec. This last case concerned a woman who underwent an
operation in 1889 for an ulcerated tongue which had been diagnosed as cancerous. After three months she suffered a recurrence of trouble, with swollen lymph glands in the neck, pain in
the ears and symptoms of toxaemia. As usual, one wonders
whether the supposed recurrence was anything more than an
infective process. The striking 'before and after' photographs
of this case reproduced in Le Bec's *Raisons Médicales de croire au
Miracle* (10th ed., p. 117) are very misleading. The first photo-
graph, in spite of a caption implying the contrary, appears to
represent the condition before the patient had surgical treatment, not the condition as it was when she went to Lourdes.

(4) RAPID HEALING WOUNDS

Many Lourdes cases have achieved notoriety because they
have been labelled with a diagnosis that implies incurability,
but since the Lourdes diagnoses are so often open to doubt on
account of lack of information or peculiarities in the history
and symptoms, these are not necessarily the cases of greatest
medical importance. As the rather sceptical Dr Ferron has
pointed out (11), some of the most interesting Lourdes cases
are the abnormally swift cures of infected wounds, for in these
cases the healing process can be observed directly by any competent witness. One of the official miracles, that of Colonel
Pellegrin, was of this nature, but it was not a very striking

example. There are better instances to be found among the
older reports. Two such will suffice to illustrate the point,
although there are others equally suggestive.

First, the case of Mlle Marie Borel, reported by Boissarie (5),
and quoted by many later writers, including Dom Francis Izard
(15). Mlle Borel, a very pious woman, who shortly after entered a convent, was taken to Lourdes in August, 1907. For
six years—ever since an operation for appendicitis—she had
suffered from recurrent abdominal abscesses resulting in fistulae
communicating with the intestines. She had a persistent discharge of pus and intestinal material from her open wounds. In
fact her condition had been getting worse and worse, and the
surgeon of the hospital where she was a patient, Dr Bardol,
wrote describing her cure as 'contrary to all expectation'. Her
illness has been described as 'probably tuberculous' (Izard). Be
this as it may, one can readily concur that before the age of
chemotherapy pyostercoral fistulae of such chronicity, whatever their origin, would scarcely be expected to heal at all, far
less to clear up all of a sudden.

Mlle Borel arrived on August 17th, and Mlle Arnaud de
Pistoris, who dressed her wounds that day, describes six actively
discharging fistulae, four of them passing faeces. In the days
following, the discharge lessened, the wounds began to close,
and Mlle Borel felt better and was able to take food, but she
lacked the strength to walk. On the morning of August 22nd,
when she was immersed in the pool, she cried out loudly that
she was cured and started to walk about. The same day she
visited the Medical Bureau where her wounds were noted to
be firmly closed and dry and photographs were taken. She
rapidly gained weight and strength, and in 1911, still in good
health, she gave evidence before a Canonical Commission that
resulted in her cure being pronounced miraculous. One interesting point: Mlle Borel had been taking morphine, and
although she no longer suffered any discomfort after her cure,
she was unable to overcome immediately a restless craving for
the drug, the doses of which had to be reduced gradually.
(Compare the similar experience of Mme Rose Martin.)

Another case of extraordinarily rapid healing of discharging abscesses is that of Lydia Brosse. The account is taken from Dr Vallet's published version (42, p. 132). Mlle Brosse, born October, 1889, entered hospital at St. Raphael in April, 1929, suffering from intestinal and nasal haemorrhages and pus in the urine. The head of the right radius bone, and part of the middle finger of the right hand had been amputated on account of infection of the bones, presumably tuberculous. In January, 1930 she develops an abscess of the inguinal region, which has to be drained. Then multiple abscesses of the buttocks form, which have to be repeatedly incised. There is abundant suppuration and sloughing of tissue. The details are given by Dr Chabal, one of the hospital doctors, who adds:

October, 1930 her condition was lamentable, the ulceration of the buttocks very deep, with abundant sloughing and suppuration. Another large abscess formed which had to be opened. Her weight was 39 kg. 100. There was also profound anaemia.

She was taken to Lourdes lying prone, abscesses suppurating and in great pain. She was bathed on October 8th, 9th and 10th without any improvement being noted. On the last occasion, the attendants at the pool considered her too ill for immersion, so they simply applied cloths soaked in Lourdes water. On October 11th, during the train journey back from Lourdes, she felt better. Profiting by this respite, the nurses changed her dressing, which was soaked in pus as usual. Later, Dr Vernejoul, the doctor in charge of the pilgrimage train, looked at the buttocks again and found that they were healing and that the dressings were no longer impregnated with pus. By the time she reached her destination she was able to get up and move about briskly. Next day she was examined at the hospital by Dr Clement who certifies that epithelialization was not quite complete, but the incision wounds were closed up, all inflammation had subsided and the large gluteal abscess had disappeared. A few days later she was re-examined by Dr Chabal who could find nothing but large healthy scars. Mlle Brosse rapidly regained weight and health, and Dr Vallet reported in 1936 that her health was still excellent.

If one can accept the veracity of the reported facts (and this

is a very big 'if' in view of the considerations previously discussed), the cases of Borel and Brosse provide evidence of an
unexpected and powerful curative factor. That such wounds
should heal is not intrinsically impossible—like the regeneration of dead nerve cells or the reformation of excised
organs—but in these cases the natural healing process seems
to have been given unusual impetus. The process itself was
normal enough, beginning with the cessation of suppuration
and ending in scar formation, but in view of the presence of
long-standing infection, the healing in these cases was most
unexpectedly swift and complete. The question arises whether
such swift healing is ever observed apart from Lourdes.

LeCron states: 'Although never scientifically proved, many
authorities believe that the rate of healing of a wound or injury
can be materially accelerated by hypnotic suggestion.' (20,
p. 282). There is ample experimental evidence that vasomotor-
reactions, blood-pressure, heart and respiration rates, and many
aspects of blood chemistry can be profoundly influenced both by
spontaneous emotional reactions and also more dramatically by
means of emotional responses artificially induced under hypnosis (35). There is thus some rational physiological basis
for the belief that healing processes can be so influenced. Early
workers in hypnosis, such as Liébault and Bernheim, made extraordinary claims for hypnotic cures of organic disease. Their
reports have fallen into disrepute, and their 'cures' have been
explained as temporary remissions or faulty diagnoses, but one
hesitates to dismiss these observations altogether. Earlier in
this book (p. 19) some instances were quoted of the swift
alleviation of very severe skin lesions by psychological treatment. But tuberculous lesions are generally slow in their
response to any influence except the newest antibiotics, and I
know of no recorded case of tuberculous abscesses and fistulae
clearing up as a result of psychological treatment in the way
Lydia Brosse's troubles cleared up at Lourdes, although one
would hesitate to declare that such an event would be intrinsically impossible. But we need not make too much of the Borel
and Brosse cases, for no bacteriological evidence is offered to
prove that the wounds really were infected with tuberculosis at

the time of the healing. In these, as in so many other Lourdes cases, one is left with the impression that, although something of interest may be happening, the medical observations are so sketchy and inadequate we shall never know for sure.

VI

CONCLUSION

'Entre le fait miraculeux et la critique scientifique, une faille se découvre, que seule la foi peut combler. Comme le dit Jean Hellé: "La foi franchit le pas auquel se refuse la science."'—Dr Jean Lhermitte (23).

THOSE who have had the patience to follow through this long examination may well wonder whether it has all been worth while. From the outset it was pointed out that no firm scientific conclusions could be drawn from the sort of sporadic clinical observations on exceptional cases that are made at Lourdes. Clinical judgment gives the doctor, who is forced to do something to help his patient, a basis for choosing between different treatments, but scientific research demands more objective standards. In the absence of a research team investigating whole groups of pilgrims with the aid of laboratory tests and measurements, one cannot be sure that a special curative factor even exists, much less find out how it works. But in spite of the fact that the kind of observations at present made at Lourdes can never hope to carry great scientific weight, the subject has attracted widespread and serious public interest. For this reason, if for no other, it has been a task worth doing to set out, in terms comprehensible to the general reader, an analysis and appraisal of the evidence, such as it is, that the Lourdes Medical Bureau offers to the world.

The conclusions to be drawn have already been indicated, and can be summed up very quickly. The rarity of the cures, and the incompleteness of the medical information on most of the cases put forward as miracles, makes any kind of appraisal exceedingly difficult. As far as it goes, and taking the dossiers at their face value, the evidence for anything 'miraculous' in the popular sense of the expression is extremely meagre. Self-evidently impossible cures, involving something like the regeneration of a lost eye or limb, are not in question because they are never claimed. The great majority of the cures concern potentially recoverable conditions and are remarkable only in the speed and manner in which they are said to have taken place. In no case is a sudden structural change confirmed by the objective evidence of X-rays taken just before and just after the event. In spite of his willingness to accept some Lourdes cures as seemingly inexplicable, Dr Ferron makes this point very clearly in his Thesis (11).

The nature of the published cures gives some indication of their probable explanations. Chronic incapacitating states in unmarried women predominate. Tuberculous peritonitis is a favourite, but the diagnosis is usually open to doubt. Psychosomatic factors as well as plain hysteria must play a considerable part. Cures of cancer are very rarely claimed in recent years, and such cases as are advanced lack microscopical confirmation of the diagnosis of the current condition—although the patients may well have had genuine cancer previously successfully treated by surgical removal.

Close examination of the eleven modern miracle cases yields scant indication of any absolutely inexplicable recovery. Some are in fact readily explained in ordinary terms and only appear as evidence of the supernormal by virtue of over-enthusiastic interpretations and much special pleading on the part of the authorities responsible for putting them forward. A prominent functional component is evident in some of the miracle cases (e.g. Clauzel, Gestas). Considering the large numbers of sick pilgrims and the energy expended on substantiating claims it is surprising that puzzling cases are not more numerous.

Even taking them at their face value the facts put forward provide a very weak basis for the claims made. And, indeed, in view of the bias and unreliability shown in some instances, it is difficult not to feel real hesitancy as to the trustworthiness of the facts in general. Some of the published versions of cures (Gérard B. was a glaring example) appear so garbled and and exaggerated as amply to justify an initial attitude of critical scepticism in approaching all the statements of the Lourdes Medical Bureau.

In a short paper on parapsychological healing the psychoanalyst, Dr Michael Balint, put his finger neatly on the root of the trouble with the Medical Bureau (1). Some of the criteria that cases must comply with to be accepted by the Church as miracles are unrealistic. Recovery must be instantaneous and involve a sudden change from severe illness to full health with no intervening period of convalescence. There must be physical signs of the change. Dr Balint comments: 'To every medically trained man it is obvious that these criteria are grossly exaggerated, i.e. ambivalently idealized. They correspond only to very old and profound human desires, but never to reality. If they have to be applied to real cases, all sorts of allowances have to be made and subterfuges tolerated.'

Concern with these criteria, and the necessity to distort facts to fit them in, so occupies the minds of the doctors concerned in the preparation of the Lourdes dossiers that they fail utterly to preserve that detached frame of mind so essential to a fair consideration of the respective merits of all possible interpretations. Their weakness is that, being impelled to arrive at a predetermined goal, they cannot let themselves be carried along by the facts, but must strive to carry the facts with them. Again and again, in reading their accounts, I have felt that if only they had shown the same enthusiasm for collecting data and investigating alternative diagnoses as they show in devising ingenious arguments to force the reader into their own line of thought, then they might really have produced some worthwhile evidence.

Although the evidence at present available fails to carry conviction, this does not mean that swift and profound physiological changes do not sometimes take place as a result of a visit to Lourdes. In the present writer's opinion such changes are quite possible, and some of the old cases of rapid healing of infected wounds (e.g. Lydia Brosse) are of greater interest in this connection than most of the modern miracles. Unfortunately the rarity of these events, and the context in which they occur, make objective observations by outsiders peculiarly difficult. But if one result of this report is to stimulate the Lourdes Medical Bureau to redouble their efforts, and to concentrate on scientific studies of whole groups of sick pilgrims, instead of wasting time bolstering up uncertain interpretations with authoritarian pronouncements, then I shall feel content. The labour of this report, and the unpleasantness of expressing harsh views about the judgment of colleagues of greater standing and experience in the profession, will not have been in vain.

APPENDIX

CURES ACCEPTED BY THE LOURDES MEDICAL BUREAU
IN THE PERIOD 1925-50

This list has been compiled from the published sources indicated. The figures in brackets refer to the numbers in the list of references. Cures are not published until some time has elapsed and more recent cases are not available. The * indicates that the case appears among the collection of names and photographs exhibited in the foyer of the Lourdes Medical Bureau.

Name:	Illness attributed to:	References
1925		
Mlle Marie Louise Arnaud	Disseminated sclerosis	(15 (41)
Sister Marie D'Assise, *née* Thérèse Mounier	Pulmonary T.B.	(41) (42)
1926[1]		
Mlle Delot	Malignant pyloric ulcer	(5) (21) (43)
Mlle Julia Hotois	Gastric ulcer	(21)
Mme A. Augault	Complications of uterine fibromata	(32)
1927		
Mme Eugénie Desgrée	Urinary retention, urethritis	(41)
Mlle Yvonne Hanselin	T.B. enteritis	(41)
Mlle Suzanne Gestas	T.B. peritonitis	(41)
Mlle Marie Ramond (Mère Marie-Joseph)	T.B. peritonitis	(41)
Henri Mieuzet	T.B. entero-colitis	(41)
Mlle Jeanne Bonvarlet	Cervical glands and fistulae	(41)
Mlle Marie Laplaud	Polyvisceral T.B.	(41)
Mme Françoise Marsat	Dorso-lumbar Pott's and pyelonephritis	(41)
Sister Marie Joseph Bosseau	T.B. laryngitis	(41)
1928		
Gilbert Clot (child)	Broncho-pneumonia	(41)
Mlle Pochet	Pulmonary T.B.	(41)
M. Auguste Aerts	Purulent angio-cholecystitis with biliary fistula	(41)
Mlle Marie Annie Sophie Heuschen	T.B. intestine, knee and kidney	(41)
Sister Marie Alysia	Pott's Disease	(41)
M. Viannes	Intestinal haemorrhage	(41)
Mlle Josephine Michel	Pott's Disease with paraplegia	(41)

[1] Unfortunately Dr Vallet's book, *Guérisons de Lourdes en 1926*, is out of print and not available in the Bibliothèque Nationale.

Name:	*Illness attributed to:*	*References*
Mlle Yvonne Mondine	Pulmonary T.B.	(41)
Mme Fernande Lelong	Pott's Disease with abscess	(41)
M. l'abbé D.	Pulmonary T.B. and T.B. laryngitis	(41) (16) (15)
Mlle Jeanne Benech	Gastric ulcer	(41)
Mlle Germaine Desfontis	Pulmonary T.B.	(41)
M. Théophile Thiem	Post-gastrectomy gastric fistula	(41)
Mlle Odette Soumagnac	Encephalitis lethargica	

1929

Mlle Paulette Margerie	T.B. meningitis	(4) (42)
Mme Marie Grassi	Post-gastrectomy complications	(42)
Mlle Marie Chauvin	Cervical Pott's Disease	(42)
Julienne Tourcoing	Gastric ulcer	(*)
Irene Van de Voorde	Pulmonary T.B.	(*)
Marguerite Adam	Renal T.B.	(*)
M. l'abbé Lochet	Pulmonary and cardiac insufficiency (War gas)	(43)

1930

Mlle Lydia Brosse	Multiple T.B. abscesses of buttocks	(42) (43) (15)
Lucie Roisin	Chronic entero-colitis	(*)
Antoinette Sicre	Chronic cholecystitis, nephritis	(*)
Emily Lingrie	Dorsal Pott's Disease	(*)
Germaine Gary	Bilateral renal T.B.	(*)
Mlle Lucienne Leclerc	T.B. peritonitis	(42)

1931

E. Invernizzi	Actinomycosis	(*)
Angelo Rimpot	Dorsal Pott's Disease	(*)
Ambroisine Jaine	T.B. arthritis, fistulae	(*)
Henriette Carpentier	Pott's Disease	(*)
Mme Doudart	Partial monoplegia from encephalitis	(*)

1932

M. Antoine Rodriguez	Dorso-lumbar Pott's Disease	(*)
Bernadette Vignes	Pulmonary T.B.	(*)
Mme Pierson	Sequelae of encephalitis	(*)
Alice Guy	T.B. fistulae	(*)
C. Brencolinni	T.B. nephritis	(*)

1933

R. Leducq	Pott's Disease	(*)
Mlle Augustine Levrot	T.B. peritonitis	(42) (*)
Georgette Bourton	Abdominal fistula	(*)
Yves Joucan (child)	Cervical Pott's Disease	(42) (*)
Marie Engel	Pulmonary T.B.	(*)
Betty Fratteur	Dorsal Pott's Disease	(*)
Mlle Hélène Perdereau	Pulmonary and peritoneal T.B.	(42) (*)

Name:	*Illness attributed to:*	*References*
Mlle Lydie LeHericy	T.B. arthritis	(42) (*)
Mlle Eugenie Marionnaud	T.B. abscess and fistula	(42)
Sister Noemi *née* Maria Record	Right sacro-coxalgia	(42)

1934

M. Fernand Legrand	Ascending polyneuritis, myelitis	(42) (*)
Adèle Degoile	Meningo-encephalitis	(*)
Sister M. Giry	Lumbar Pott's Disease	(*)
M. l'abbé Paul Flavigny	Stercoral fistula of ileum	(42) (*)
Mlle Madeline Guinot	Pulmonary T.B. Pott's Disease	(16) (42) (*)
M. R. Guyot	Perinephritic abscess	(*)

1935

René Chavel	Brachial paralysis	(*)
Adolphe Mortraux	Multiple fractures	(*)
Mlle Madeleine Fenault	Gastric ulcer	(43)

1936

Mlle Odette Rivière	Ileo-caecal T.B.	(43)
Charles Macdonald	Pott's Disease. Renal T.B.	(27) (43)
Mme Marguerite Pouxveille	Gastric ulcer	(15)

1937

Mlle Louise Jamain (proclaimed miraculous)	Pulmonary T.B.	(43) (16) (13)
Sister Marie Marguerite (proclaimed miraculous)	Nephritis	(17)
Mlle Mirelle Préclin	Vesical, renal and peritoneal T.B.	(*)
Sister St. Marguerite	T.B. abscess of neck	(*)
Mme Madeleine Quartier	Coronary atheroma, angina pectoris	(43)
Mme Germaine Bristen	T.B. of joints and kidney	(43)
Mlle Madeleine Loyer	Paralysis of right leg. Right hemi-anaesthesia	(43)
Mlle Yvett Conen	Subacute malignant endocarditis	(43)
Mlle Angelina de Giovanni	Septico-pyaemia	(43)
Mlle Viviane Brouilly	Cervical arthritis	(43)

1938

Sister Clothilde	T.B. peritonitis	(*)
Francis Pascal (child) (proclaimed miraculous)	Optic atrophy	(22)

1941

Mlle Marguerite Malgoyne	Pulmonary, peritoneal and renal T.B.	(*) (22)

1943

Mlle Gabrielle Clauzel (proclaimed miraculous)	Rheumatic spondylitis with compression of nerve roots	(22)

Name:	Illness attributed to	References
1945		
Mlle Yvonne Fournier	Traumatic paralysis of arm	(*)
1946		
Guy Leydet (child)	Quadriplegia and post-encephalitic idiocy	(22)
1947		
Gérard Baillie (child)	Chorio-retinitis	(22)
Mme Rose Martin (proclaimed miraculous)	Secondary carcinoma	(22)
Mlle Marie Thérèse Canin (proclaimed miraculous)	T.B. peritonitis	
Mlle Ernestine Gibault	Vestibular syndrome with deafness	(22)
Mme Gestas (proclaimed miraculous)	Adhesions from gastrectomy	
1948		
Mlle Jeanne Fretel (proclaimed miraculous)	T.B. peritonitis	(22)
1950		
Fräulein Traute Fulda (proclaimed miraculous)	Addison's Disease	
Colonel Pellegrin (proclaimed miraculous)	Liver abscess and fistula	
Signor Evasio Ganora	Hodgkin's Disease	

Kilogram. 2.2 pounds.

Koch's Bacillus. The germ responsible for tuberculosis.

Kyphosis. Curvature of the spine, bent back.

Laparotomy. Surgical operation to explore inside the abdomen.

Lipiodol. Oily substance, opaque to X-rays, used for making cavities show up on X-ray photos.

Lumbar region. Lower back.

Lymphocytes. One type of white blood cell.

Lymphocytic meningitis. An infection of the meninges, or lining membranes of the brain, in which large numbers of lymphocytes are present.

Maxilla. Upper jaw.

Meningitis. Inflammation of the meninges or lining membranes of the brain and spinal cord.

Meteorism. Distension of the abdomen with gas or air.

Myoclonic attacks. Convulsive muscular jerks.

Neoplasm. New growth, cancer, tumour.

Nystagmus, Nystagmiform movements. Involuntary oscillations of the eyes.

Oedema. Swelling due to fluid in tissues.

Oesophagus. Gullet.

Optic atrophy. Degeneration of the optic nerve, leading to blindness.

Optic atrophy, post-neuritic type. Optic atrophy following an inflammatory reaction of the optic nerve.

Optic disc. Area at the back of the eye, visible by means of an ophthalmoscope, where optic nerve enters eye.

Optic nerve. Main nerve of the eye on which vision depends.

Osteitis. Inflammation of bone.

Osteophytic proliferation. Formation of new bone tissue stimulated by inflammation.

Papilloedema. Swollen appearance of optic disc.

Paraplegia. Paralysis of lower limbs.

Parenchyma. The essential tissue of an organ, as opposed to the supportive and connective tissues.

P.A.S. Antibiotic used for tuberculosis.

Peritoneum. Lining membranes of the abdomen.

Peritonitis. Inflammation of the peritoneum.

Pleura. Lining membranes of the lungs.

Pleurisy. Inflammation of the pleura.

Pneumothorax. Introduction of air into one side of the chest to collapse a lung in the treatment of tuberculosis.

Polymorph cells. A type of white blood cell that appears in great numbers at the site of purulent infection.

Pott's Disease. Tuberculosis of the spine.

Precordial. Over the heart.

Ptosis. Drooping, especially of eyelids.

Pyonephritis. Purulent inflammation of the kidney.

Rales. Noises in the chest heard through the stethoscope and indicative of lung disease.

Rectoscopy. Examination of the interior of the lower bowel by the insertion of an instrument permitting direct inspection.

Retina. The light-sensitive layer of the eye.

Rheumatoid arthritis. Joint inflammation of a particular type.

Root Pains. Characteristic shooting pains due to the compression of nerves at their point of entry to the spinal column.

Sacro-iliac Joint. Joint between hip bone and sacrum.

Sacrum. Base of spine.

Scoliosis. Lateral curvature of spine.

Sigmoid colon. Part of the large bowel.

Spastic. Stiff due to muscle spasm.

Splenic angle. A region of the colon of large bowel.

Spondylitis. Inflammation of bones of spine.

Stoma. Orifice.

Strabismus. Squint.

Strangulating Hernia. A protrusion so constricted at its base as to cut off its blood supply and threaten gangrene.

Tendon reflexes. Responses, such as the knee jerk, produced by tapping tendons and used to test for neurological disease.

Vertebrae. Bones of the spine.

Vertebral Discs. Discs of cartilage between the vertebrae.

Vertebral Lippings. Ridges on the borders of the vertebral bodies, indicative of arthritis of the spine.

Vesicular Murmur. Soft breath sounds heard through the stethoscope.

Visual Field. Scope of vision without moving the eyes.

Xiphoid Process. Lower extremity of breast bone.